Grade 1

Scott Foresman

Reader's and Writer's Notebook
Teacher's Manual

PEARSON

Glenview, Illinois • Boston, Massachusetts • Chandler, Arizona •
Upper Saddle River, New Jersey

ISBN 13: 978-0-328-48475-1
ISBN 10:   0-328-48475-X

1 2 3 4 5 6 7 8 9 10 V011 18 17 16 15 14 13, 12 11 10 09

Readiness: My World

Unit 1: Animals, Tame and Wild

Unit 2: Communities

Unit 3: Changes

Unit 4: Treasures

Unit 5: Great Ideas

Name _____

Unit R Reading Log

Reading Time	Title and Author	What is it about?	How would you rate it?	Why?
From ____ to ____			Great OK Awful	
From ____ to ____			Great OK Awful	
From ____ to ____			Great OK Awful	
From ____ to ____			Great OK Awful	
From ____ to ____			Great OK Awful	

Name _____

Unit 1 Reading Log

Reading Time	Title and Author	What is it about?	How would you rate it?	Why?
From _____ to _____			Great OK Awful	
From _____ to _____			Great OK Awful	
From _____ to _____			Great OK Awful	
From _____ to _____			Great OK Awful	
From _____ to _____			Great OK Awful	

Name _____

Unit 2 Reading Log

Reading Time	Title and Author	What is it about?	How would you rate it?	Why?
From ___ to ___			Great OK Awful	
From ___ to ___			Great OK Awful	
From ___ to ___			Great OK Awful	
From ___ to ___			Great OK Awful	
From ___ to ___			Great OK Awful	

Name _____

Unit 3 Reading Log

Reading Time	Title and Author	What is it about?	How would you rate it?	Why?
From ____ to ____			Great OK Awful	
From ____ to ____			Great OK Awful	
From ____ to ____			Great OK Awful	
From ____ to ____			Great OK Awful	
From ____ to ____			Great OK Awful	

Name _____

Unit 4 Reading Log

Reading Time	Title and Author	What is it about?	How would you rate it?	Why?
From ____ to ____			Great OK Awful	
From ____ to ____			Great OK Awful	
From ____ to ____			Great OK Awful	
From ____ to ____			Great OK Awful	
From ____ to ____			Great OK Awful	

Name _____

Unit 5 Reading Log

Reading Time	Title and Author	What is it about?	How would you rate it?	Why?
From ____ to ____			Great OK Awful	
From ____ to ____			Great OK Awful	
From ____ to ____			Great OK Awful	
From ____ to ____			Great OK Awful	
From ____ to ____			Great OK Awful	

Name _____

Story Title _____

Author _____

> A **picture walk** can help you learn about a story.

Look at the pictures in the story. What do you want to find out about the story?

Draw a picture of the thing or person you have a question about.

Check children's drawings.

Who is the character in the story? **How** does the character feel or act? **Write**.

_____

Sam; Check children's responses. Accept all

responsible responses.

Name _____

Story Title _____

Author _____

You can look at the pictures in a story and **predict** what might happen in the story.

You can **set a purpose** for reading by thinking about why you want to read this story.

Look at the pictures in the story.
What do you predict about the story?
Draw a picture about your prediction. **Write** a label about it.

Check children's drawings.

Check your predictions. **Read** the part that tells in the story.

Write where the story takes place.

Check children's work.

Read
Together

Name _____

Story Title _____

Author _____

Circle the sentences that are true about realistic fiction.

It has animals that talk like people.

(There are characters.)

(It has a setting.)

(It tells about things that could really happen.)

Draw pictures to show what happens at the beginning, the middle, and end of the story.

	Check children's drawings.	

Name _____

Story Title _____

Author _____

You can **ask questions** about what you are going to read to better understand the story.

Look at the pictures in the story. What **questions** would you like to ask about the characters and events in the story? **Write.**

_____

Check children's questions.

_____

_____

_____

_____

_____

_____

_____

_____

Circle each sentence that tells about realistic fiction.

(It is a made up story that could happen in real life.)

It is a story that could not happen.

(There are one or more characters in the story.)

(It has a beginning, middle and end.)

Read Together

Name _____

Story Title _____

Author _____

Look at the pictures of the story. **Think** about what you know about the topic. **Write** a question about the story.

_____

Check children's questions.

_____

_____

Then **reread** the part of the story that answers your question. Did you have to make any corrections to your question?

What happened in the story? **Draw** the problem or the solution.

Check children's drawings.

Name _____

Story Title _____

Author _____

What do you think the characters in the story will see at the farmers market? **Draw** pictures and **write** labels.

Check children's drawings.

Compare this story with *Snap!*

Beginning

Check children's work.

⬇

Middle

⬇

End

Name _____

Story Title _____

Author _____

> When you read, you should understand what and why things happen in the story.
>
> **Ask questions** about the story before you read and then look for the answers in the story.

What would you do if you read a part of a story that did not make sense to you? **Write**.

_____

Accept all reasonable responses such as reread

the part that doesn't make sense.

Think about the story you just read. **Write** or **draw** what you did to understand the events in the story.

Check children's responses.

Name _____

Story Title _____

Author _____

A story can be a **fantasy**. This kind of story is made up.

Look at the pictures of the story. How do you know this is a fantasy? **Write**.

Accept all reasonable responses such as the

characters are animals that act like people act.

When you summarize a story, you tell the most important parts of the story in your own words.

Draw a picture to tell about an important event in the story.

Check children's drawings.

Name _____

Story Title _____

Author _____

Think about what you know about an ox. **Draw** a picture about how an ox can help on a farm. Write a sentence to tell about your picture.

Check children's drawings.

When you **visualize** a story, you form pictures in your mind based on the details from the story.

Check children's drawings.

Name _____

Story Title _____

Author _____

Draw a picture of a fox and a kit.

Check children's drawings.

Draw a picture of what you think was the most important event in the story.

Check children's drawings.

Name _____

Story Title _____

Author _____

Look at the cover and the title of the story. Where do you think the story takes place? **Draw** the setting. **Explain** your drawing.

Check children's drawings.

Think about the beginning, middle and end of the story. **Draw** a picture of the most important event in the story. Include the characters and setting of the story.

Check children's drawings.

Name _____

Story Title _____

Author _____

Underline the sentences that tell about literary nonfiction.

It tells information about real characters or places.

The characters are always animals.

It is a made up story

It gives information about an event.

The events of the story happened in a certain order. **Draw** a picture of what the author saw at the animal park right after she saw the zebras. **Write** a label.

Check children's drawings.

Name _____

Story Title _____

Author _____

Tell what you know about animal families. Then **look** at the pictures in the story. Predict what the story will be about and what might happen. **Write**.

Check children's responses.

_____
- -
_____
- -
_____
- -
_____

Check your predictions. **Read** the part that tells in the story. Were your predictions correct? What was surprising and why? **Write**.

Check children's responses.

_____
- -
_____
- -
_____
- -
_____
- -
_____

Name _____

Story Title _____

Author _____

When you read, you should understand what and why things happen in the story.

Ask questions about the story before you read and then look for clues in the story.

Write some questions about the story to help you better understand the story when you read.

Check children's responses.

_____

Look at the story again. What part did you not understand?
Write what you did to understand that part of the story.

Answers may vary. Accept all reasonable responses such as reread and identify clues to find the answers.

Name _____

Story Title _____

Author _____

Underline the sentences that tell about expository text.

It is a made up story.

It gives facts and details.

It can be about real people, animals or places.

It is a story that should be acted out.

_____

Write three facts you learned from reading the selection.

Check children's responses.

Name _____

Story Title _____

Author _____

What do you know about dinosaurs? **Write** about when and how dinosaurs lived.

_____

Check children's responses.

_____

- -

_____

_____

- -

_____

═══════════════════════════════════════

Think about **what you knew** about dinosaurs before you read the story. Then use what you know and the clues in the text to **tell more** about dinosaurs. **Write** a list.

Check children's responses.

Name _____

Story Title _____

Author _____

Draw a picture of an animal that lives in a forest.
Write a sentence about your picture.

Check children's drawings.

Check children's sentences.

Now **draw** your favorite forest animal. Tell the most important
things about the animal. **Write** a caption.

Check children's drawings.

Check children's sentences.

Name _____

Story Title _____

Author _____

> You can **ask questions** about what you are going to read to better understand the story.

Look at the pictures in the text. What questions would you like to ask? **Write**.

_____
Check children's questions.
_____
_____
_____
_____
_____
_____

Look for the answers to your questions in the text. **Write** the answers.

_____
Check children's responses.
_____
_____
_____
_____
_____
_____

Name _____

Story Title _____

Author _____

Draw a picture of your favorite place to play.
Why is this your favorite place? **Write** a sentence.

Check children's drawings.

Check children's responses.

Accept all reasonable responses.

Look at the picture you drew. **How** would you change it?
Add to your picture to show what you would change.

Check changes children made to their drawings.

Name _____

Story Title _____

Author _____

Circle the sentences that are true about an animal fantasy.

(The characters are animals.)

It is a story that could happen in real life.

(The animals can talk.)

(The animals act like people.)

Think about **what you knew** about animals before you read the story. **Draw** pictures to show the things you knew that helped you better understand the story.

Check children's drawings. Accept all reasonable responses.	

Name _____

Story Title _____

Author _____

Underline each sentence that is true about **expository text**.

<u>It gives facts and details.</u>

<u>It tells about real people or animals.</u>

The story may tell how make-believe characters act.

It is a play.

Think about something in the story that was hard to understand.
Write what you did to understand this part of the story.

<u>Answers may vary. Accept all reasonable</u>

<u>responses such as reread and identify clues</u>

<u>to find the answers</u>

Name _____

Story Title _____

Author _____

Draw a picture of a seed and a flower.
What can a gardener do to help the seed become a flower?
Write a sentence.

Check children's drawings.

Accept all reasonable responses.

Draw a picture of Toad in his garden once it has bloomed.
How does Toad feel about his garden? **Write** a sentence.

Check children's drawings.

Check children's responses.

© Pearson Education, Inc., 1

Name _____

Story Title _____

Author _____

Circle the sentences that are true about literary nonfiction.

It teaches a lesson.

(It describes events that happen in real life.)

(It gives information about real people or animals.)

It tells about make-believe things.

Draw pictures of three things that happen in the life cycle of a butterfly. **Write** the number 1, 2, or 3 under each picture to show the order of the events.

	Check children's drawings and numbering.	

_____ _____ _____

Name _____

Story Title _____

Author _____

Draw a picture of an animal getting ready for winter.
Write a label for the animal.
Then **write** a sentence telling what the animal is doing.

> **Check children's drawings and labels.**

Check children's responses.

Accept all reasonable responses.

How is a play different from a story? **Write.**

Check children's responses.

Accept all reasonable responses.

Name _____

Story Title _____

Author _____

What if something in the story you are about to read doesn't make sense?
Draw a picture of what you will do. **Write** a sentence about it.

Check children's drawings.

_____

Check children's responses. Accept all reasonable responses.

Think about parts of the story that didn't make sense to you.
Draw what you did to help you understand what was happening.
Write a sentence about it.

Check children's drawings.

_____

Check children's responses. Accept all reasonable responses.

© Pearson Education, Inc., 1

Name _____

Story Title _____

Author _____

Circle the sentences that are true about a fairy tale.

(The characters are magic people.)

(The story takes place long ago)

The story tells information about real events.

(The setting is in a make-believe land.)

_____

When you **visualize** a story, you form pictures in your mind based on the details from the story.

Draw a picture of Cinderella's dress or her coach. Write a label.

Check children's drawings and labels.

Name _____

Story Title _____

Author _____

Draw a picture of a place you have visited on a trip.
Write a sentence about the thing you liked best about the place.

Check children's drawings.

Check children's responses. Accept all reasonable responses.

What did you learn from the story? **Write** two or three facts.

Check children's responses. Accept all reasonable responses.

Name _____

Story Title _____

Author _____

What questions do you have about life on a ranch?
Write your questions.

Check children's questions.

_____

When you read, you should look for answers to your questions. Remember that sometimes a story will not answer every question.

Look at the questions you wrote before reading the story.
Write answers to as many questions as you can.

Check children's responses.

Accept all reasonable responses.

Name _____

Story Title _____

Author _____

Draw a picture of your favorite thing from when you were a baby. **Why** was it your favorite? **Write** a sentence.

Check children's drawings.

_____
- -
 Check children's responses. Accept all reasonable responses.

A **fiction story** has three parts. It has a beginning, a middle, and an end.

Think about the story you just read. **How** did knowing about the parts of a story help you understand what was happening? **Write** sentences to explain.

_____
- -
 Check children's responses. Accept all reasonable responses.
_____
- -
_____
- -
_____

Name _____

Story Title _____

Author _____

Look at the pictures in the story.
Write what you predict will happen in the story.

_____

Check children's predictions.

_____

- -

_____

Think about why you want to read this story.
Write a purpose for reading it.

_____

Check children's purposes.

_____

- -

_____

Check your prediction. **Read** the part in the story that tells
what did happen.
Write a sentence telling if your prediction was correct or not.

_____

- -

_____

- -

_____

Name _____

Story Title _____

Author _____

When you read, you should understand what and why things happen in the story. **Look for clues** in the pictures before you read and then read to find out what the clues mean.

What will you do if you don't understand what you read?
Write a sentence.

_____
Check children's responses. Accept all reasonable responses.
_____
_____
_____

You wrote what you would do if you didn't understand part of a story. **Reread** what you wrote above. If you did this, **write** how it helped you. If you did something else, **write** how that helped you

_____
Check children's responses. Accept all reasonable responses.
_____
_____
_____
_____
_____
_____
_____

Name _____

Story Title _____

Author _____

Draw pictures of people taking care of their pets. How do you think the pets feel about their owners? **Write** a sentence.

> ## Check children's drawings.

_____

Accept all reasonable responses.

_____

> When you **summarize** a story, you tell the most important parts of the story in your own words.

Summarize the story you just read. **Write** two or three sentences.

_____

Check children's responses.

_____

Accept all reasonable responses.

_____

_____

_____

Name _____

Story Title _____

Author _____

What is informational fiction? **Write** a sentence.

_____

- -

Possible response: It gives information about events.

Think about another story you have read that is informational fiction. **Compare** that story with *Dot & Jabber and the Great Acorn Mystery.*

	Dot & Jabber	Title of Other Story _____
Information about Characters	Check children's	work.
Information about Events		

Did you find parts of the story that were hard to understand? **Write** what you used or would use to better understand the story.

_____

- -

Accept all reasonable responses.

_____

- -

_____

Name _____

Story Title _____

Author _____

Tell about machines that you have seen.
Where did you see those machines?
What jobs do they do? Then draw a picture
of a machine you use often.

Check children's drawings.

Summarize the story you just read. **Write** three sentences.

Check children's responses. Accept all reasonable responses.

Name _____

Story Title _____

Author _____

Look at the pictures of the story. **Think** about what you know about the topic. **Write** a question about the story.

A biography is a _____ story.   made-up   (true)

A biography gives _____ about a person's life.   (facts)   jokes

A biography tells about a _____ person.   magic   (real)

> You can think about how a **text is organized** to better understand what you are reading. Sequence is one way a text can be organized.

Write three events from Alexander Graham Bell's life. **Write** the events in the order in which they happened.

_____

Check children's work for correct order of events.

_____

_____

_____

_____

_____

_____

Name _____

Story Title _____

Author _____

Think about what you know about gardens.
What are some things that grow in gardens?
Write sentences to tell what you know.

_____

Check children's responses.

_____

Accept all reasonable responses.

_____
_____
_____

Write what you learned about how people help their communities from reading this story.

_____

Check children's responses.

_____

Accept all reasonable responses.

_____
_____
_____

© Pearson Education, Inc., 1

Name _____

Book Talk Tips

- Talk about a book you like.

- Use a loud, clear voice.

- Look at your classmates.

- Don't tell how it ends!

Directions   When you talk about a book, answer these questions.

1. What is the title of the book?

2. Who is the author?

3. What kind of book is it?

4. What other book has the author written?

5. Tell what you liked the best.

6. Tell why they should read the book.

Name _____

Before You Write

- Think about ideas with a friend.

- Ask questions to help your friend pick a good topic.

When You Revise

- Read your friend's paper out loud. Listen for what you like.

- Tell your friend three things you like. Say: "I like how you ____."

- Read your friends paper out loud again. Listen for what you do not understand.

- Ask your friend two questions that you have.

It might help to think about the:

- Title.

- Beginning

- Ending

- Words that were used

- Use of verbs, nouns, adjectives or adverbs

Name _____

Title of Writing _____

Directions   Answer these questions about what you wrote.

I. What are the two things that are best about this?

_____
- -
_____
- -
_____

2. What is one thing you could have done better?

_____
- -
_____

3. Do you like what you wrote? Why or why not?

_____
- -
_____
- -
_____

Name _____

Mm

Say the word for each picture.
Write m on the line if the word has the same first sound as .

1. m _____

2. _____

3. _____

4. m _____

5. m _____

6. _____

7. _____

8. m _____

School + Home

Home Activity Your child has reviewed words that start with *m*. Help your child think of other words with /m/ as in *map*.

Phonics Consonant *Mm/m/* **1**

Name _____

Draw your favorite character from a story you know.
Tell what the character is doing.
Tell how the character feels.

Home Activity Your child learned that characters in a story can be people or animals. As you read together, have your child tell you what he or she knows about the characters in stories.

Name _____

Trace and **write** the letters. Make sure you write your letters the correct size.

Check children's work.

School + Home

Home Activity Your child practiced writing *M* and *m*. Say names and words that begin with *M* and *m* and have your child write the correct letter each time you say a name or word.

Handwriting 3

Name _____

Circle the group that could be a real word.

1. (mat)   p2n   123   s3m   546

2. 237   e8b   476   ti9   (pan)

3. 530   213   63b   (Sam)   pp2

4. 760   (tap)   m22   310   614

Look at the first group of letters. **Circle** the group of letters that is in the same order as the first group.

5. pan   (pan)   nap   pna

6. cap   tap   (cap)   pta

7. mat   map   abt   (mat)

8. bag   bad   (bag)   dma

Home Activity Your child identified groups of letters and compared the sequence of letters in words or letter groups such as *pan, nap,* and *pna*. Write some groups of numbers and some words. Have your child pick out the words.

4   Print Awareness

Name _____

Ss

Say the word for each picture.
Write s on the line if the word has the same first sound as .

1. sandwich __ s __	2. seesaw __ s __
3. socks __ s __	4. motorcycle _____
5. hat _____	6. sun __ s __
7. map _____	8. submarine __ s __

School + Home

Home Activity Your child learned that some words begin with the letter s. Have your child find other words with /s/ as in seal.

Phonics Consonant Ss/s/ **5**

Nouns: People, Animals, and Things

A **noun** names a person, an animal, or a thing.

The word **boy**
names a person.

The word **cat**
names an animal.

The word **bed**
names a thing.

Circle the correct noun for each picture.
Say a sentence for each noun.

boy   (girl)

(car)   bus

pig   (dog)

(mom)   dad

 Home Activity Your child learned about nouns that name people or things. Take turns with your child pointing to people and things in your home and saying the nouns that name them.

Name _____

Trace and **write** the letters. Make sure you write your letters the correct size.

S   s

S   S   S

Ŝ   Ŝ   Ŝ

Check children's work.

Home Activity Your child practiced writing *S* and *s*. Have your child cut out pictures from old magazines of objects that begin with *s* and paste them onto a sheet of paper and label each with the letter *s*.

Name _____

Circle the group that could be a real word.

1. 3576   (bike)   t31m   1234   o47l

2. (road)   2021   88bt   976a   54em

3. 2631   3142   987c   mm32   (pony)

4. 4226   K310   (look)   n325   7624

Look at the first group of letters. **Circle** the group of letters that is in the same order as the first group.

5. nap   (nap)   pna   pan

6. tap   pat   (tap)   apt

7. mad   dam   (mad)   mda

8. pin   nip   (pin)   imp

Home Activity Your child identified groups of letters and compared the sequence of letters in words or letter groups such as *pat, tap,* and *apt*. Write the letters of your child's name in different orders. Have your child identify the name with the letters in correct sequence.

© Pearson Education, Inc., 1

Name _____

Tt

Say the word for each picture.
Write **t** on the line if the word has the same first sound as .

1. _____ **t** _____

2. _____ _____

3. _____ _____

4. _____ **t** _____

5. _____ **t** _____

6. _____ _____

7. _____ _____

8. **10** _____ **t** _____

School + Home

Home Activity Your child learned that some words begin with the letter *t*. Have your child find other words with /t/ as in *tiger*.

Phonics Consonant Tt/t/   **9**

Name _____

Read the words in the box.
Pick a word to finish each sentence.
Write it on the line.

I   see   a   green

I. This is _____ **a** _____ .

2. We _____ **see** _____ a .

3. This is my _____ **green** _____ .

4. _____ **I** _____ am a .

School + Home

Home Activity This week your child learned to identify and read the words *I, see, a,* and *green.* As you read with your child, encourage him or her to point out these words in print.

Nouns: People, Animals, and Things

Tell about your room.
Finish the sentences.
Use words from the box or your own words.

| a bed | a rug | a lamp | books | a cat |

I have <u>**Answers will vary. Possible answers: I have a bed in my room. I have toys in my room. I have a desk in my room.**</u> in my room.

I have _____ in my room.

I have _____ in my room.

Find other nouns. **Say** a sentence for each noun.

Home Activity Your child learned how to use nouns for people and things in writing. Have your child write a sentence about people and things in another room in your home. Ask your child to identify the nouns in the sentence.

Name _____

Trace and **write** the letters. Make sure you write your letters the correct size.

Check children's work.

© Pearson Education, Inc., 1

School + Home **Home Activity** Your child practiced writing *T* and *t*. Say names and words that begin with *T* and *t* and have your child write the correct letter each time you say a name or word.

Name _____

Circle the group that could be a real word.

1. 5628   (history)   s42p   12345   u572

2. 3023   (science)   66cv   786i   63fn

3. 6432   3543   786d   (number)   kk41

4. 2435   S221   (woman)   m245   6734

Look at the first group of letters. Circle the group of letters that is in the same order as the first group.

5. pit   (pit)   tip   pti

6. sag   ags   gas   (sag)

7. nip   imp   (nip)   pin

8. tip   pit   tpi   (tip)

Home Activity Your child identified groups of letters and compared the sequence of letters in words or letter groups such as such as *pit, tip,* and *pti*. Make individual letter cards with the letters of your child's name. Ask your child to put the letters in correct sequence.

© Pearson Education, Inc., 1

Name _____

Aa

Say the word for each picture.
Write **a** on the line if the word has the same first sound as .

1. **a**

2. **a**

3.

4.

5. **a**

6.

Say the word for each picture.
Write **a** on the line to complete the word.

7. **s a t**

8. **m a t**

© Pearson Education, Inc., 1

 Home Activity Your child learned about the short *a* vowel sound in words. Have your child find other words with /a/ at the beginning or in the middle, such as *apple* and *pat*.

Name _____

Sam

Read the story.
Draw the most important character from the story.

Blue Jay found some beautiful peacock feathers.

Blue Jay tied the feathers to his tail.

He thought he looked grand.

He strutted in front of the other jays.

The jays pulled out his peacock feathers.

Then they all flew away from Blue Jay.

Blue Jay knew then: No one likes a showoff.

Drawing should be a bird with or without peacock feathers, or other pretty feathers, tied to its tail.

© Pearson Education, Inc., 1

Home Activity Your child read a fable (fiction) and identified the main character. Read a fiction story with your child. Have your child name the most important character (or characters) in the story. Ask your child to tell you what the character looks like and how the character acts.

Genre/Literary Analysis 15

Name _____

Nouns: People, Animals, and Things

Mark the sentence that has a line under a noun that names a person, an animal, or a thing.

1. ○ They <u>sat</u> on the bed.
   ○ They sat <u>on</u> the bed.
   ⊗ They sat on the <u>bed</u>.

2. ⊗ She is with her <u>mom</u>.
   ○ <u>She</u> is with her mom.
   ○ She <u>is</u> with her mom.

3. ○ He can read <u>a</u> book.
   ⊗ He can read a <u>book</u>.
   ○ He can <u>read</u> a book.

4. ○ The boy <u>plays</u> with a pet.
   ○ The boy plays <u>with</u> a pet.
   ⊗ The boy plays with a <u>pet</u>.

© Pearson Education, Inc., 1

School + Home

Home Activity Your child prepared for taking tests on nouns for people or things. Read a story together. Have your child point out nouns that name people or things in the story.

Name _____

Circle the front cover.

Sam

Sam

Place an X over the back cover.

The cat got up.

Circle the book that Sam wrote.

The Sad Cat by Sam

My Cat by Dan

School + Home

Home Activity Your child learned to identify the front cover, back cover, and title page of a book. Have your child point out the front and back covers and title page of the next book you read together.

Name _____

Trace and **write** the letters. Make sure you write your letters the correct size.

 A A A

a a a

Check children's work.

Copy the words. **Write** the letters from left to right.

Sam   Tam

mat <u>mat</u>   sat

am <u>am</u>   at <u>at</u>

as   Matt

Home Activity Your child practiced writing words with *Aa*. Have your child draw a picture of two of the words he or she wrote and label the pictures with the words.

© Pearson Education, Inc., 1

Name _____

Circle the group that could be a real word.

1. 9546   r2nf   23456   (match)   t4ms

2. 6237   (pancake)   e9bg   5769   oh77

3. (girls)   2531   9213   43cd   jj33

4. 8762   2310   (table)   n22p   5148

Look at the first group of letters. **Circle** the group of letters that is in the same order as the first group.

5. pot   (pot)   top   opt

6. ten   net   (ten)   ent

7. bat   tab   abt   (bat)

8. sat   tar   sta   (sat)

Home Activity Your child looked at the letter sequence in words and compared the sequence of letters in words or letter groups such as *pot, top,* and *opt*. Look at item 1 with your child. Have your child explain his answer.

Name _____

Read the words in the box.
Pick a word to finish each sentence.
Write it on the line.

I   see   a   green

1. ___**I**___ have a .

2. The is ___**green**___ .

3. I ___**see**___ the .

4. This is ___**a**___ .

School + Home

Home Activity This week your child identified and read the words *I, see, a,* and *green.* Write each word on a card. Have your child read each word and then use it in a sentence.

Name _____

Cc

Say the word for each picture.
Write c on the line if the word has the same first sound as .

1. _____ **c** _____

2. _____

3. _____

4. _____ **c** _____

5. _____ **c** _____

6. _____ **c** _____

7. _____

8. _____ **c** _____

School + Home

Home Activity Your child learned that some words begin with the letter c. Have your child find other words with /k/ as in cat.

Name _____

Snap!

Look at each set of pictures.
Circle the picture that shows a place.

Home Activity Your child learned about places in a story. As you read together, have your child tell you what he or she knows about the setting of the story.

22 **Comprehension** Setting

© Pearson Education, Inc., 1

Name _____

Trace and **write** the letters. Make sure you write your letters the correct size.

Check children's work.

Copy the words. **Write** the letters from left to right.

Mac

sat

Cam

Tam

cat

tat

mat

Sam

Home Activity Your child practiced writing words with *Cc*. Have your child choose two words from the box and write them on a separate piece of paper.

© Pearson Education, Inc., 1

Name _____

Look at the first group of letters. **Circle** the group of letters that is in the same order as the first group.

1.
   top

   (top) pot opt

2.
   net

   ten (net) ent

3.
   tag

   got agt (tag)

4.
   yam

   (yam) may yma

5.
   pan

   nap (pan) npa

6.
   bag

   bga gab (bag)

© Pearson Education, Inc., 1

 School + Home **Home Activity** Your child looked at the letter sequence in words and compared the sequence of letters in words or letter groups such as *top, pot,* and *opt.* Have your child identify the sequence of letters of each pictured word. Then say the word with your child.

Name _____

Pp

Say the word for each picture.
Write **p** on the line if the word has the same first sound as .

1. p

2. p

3. _____

4. p

Say the word for each picture.
Write **p** on the line if the word has the same ending sound as .

5. ma p

6. Sa

7. ca p

8. sa

© Pearson Education, Inc., 1

 School + Home **Home Activity** Your child learned that some words begin and end with the letter *p*. Have your child find other words that begin and end with /p/.

Name _____

Nouns: Places

A **noun** also names a place.

The word **school** names a place.

The word **store** names a place.

Draw a line from the noun to the correct picture.
Say a sentence for each noun.

1. zoo

2. park

3. lake

4. library

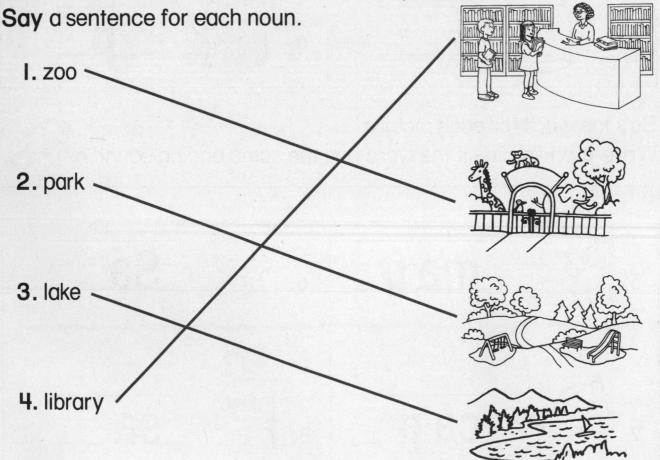

© Pearson Education, Inc., 1

Home Activity Your child learned about nouns that name places. Have your child identify places in his or her neighborhood.

Name _____

Trace and **write** the letters. Make sure you write your letters the correct size.

P   P   P

p   p   p

Check children's work.

Copy the words. **Write** the tall and small letters the correct size. **Write p** so that it falls below the line.

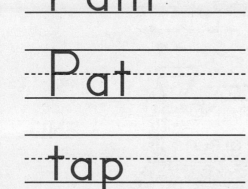

Pam   Pam   map   map

Pat   Pat   sap   sap

tap   tap   cap   cap

© Pearson Education, Inc., 1

School + Home

Home Activity Your child practiced writing words with *Pp*. Say these words to your child: *Pennsylvania, Peter, Patrick, pickle, plum, pet.* Have your child write *P* or *p* to show how each word begins.

Name _____

Trace the arrows.
Connect the word trains from left to right and top to bottom.

START:

I like green.

We see one.

See the one.

We like green.

END

© Pearson Education, Inc., 1

School + Home

Home Activity Your child learned that reading is done from top to bottom, and from left to right with a return sweep. Show your child a page from a favorite book. Have him or her point to each word from left to right, then return to the beginning of the next line and move again from left to right.

Name _____

Nn

Say the word for each picture.
Write n on the line if the word has the same first sound as .

1. n

2. _____

3. n

4. n

Say the word for each picture.
Write n on the line if the word has the same ending sound as .

5. ma

6. ca n

7. ma n

8. ca

Home Activity Your child learned that some words begin and end with the letter *n*. Have your child find other words that begin and end with /n/.

Name _____

Read the words in the box.
Pick a word to finish each sentence.
Write it on the line.

```
we      like      the      one
```

1. _____ **We** _____ see a .

2. Tip is on _____ **the** _____ .

3. I have _____ **one** _____ .

4. I _____ **like** _____ our .

© Pearson Education, Inc., 1

Home Activity This week your child identified and read the words *we, like, the,* and *one*. As you read with your child, encourage him or her to point out these words in print.

30   High-Frequency Words

Name _____

Nouns: Places

Tell about places you go with your family.
Finish the sentences.
Use words from the box or your own words.

> store   playground   park   zoo

My family and I go to the ___Answers will vary. Possible answer: My family and I go to the park.___.

My family and I go to the ___Answers will vary. Possible answer: My family and I go to the zoo.___.

My family and I go to the ___Answers will vary. Possible answer: My family and I go to the store.___.

Find other nouns. **Say** a sentence for each noun.

Home Activity Your child learned how to use nouns for places in writing. Have your child write two sentences that tell about a place he or she would like to go. Ask your child to identify the noun he or she used.

© Pearson Education, Inc., 1

Name _____

Trace and **write** the letters. Make sure you write your letters the correct size.

Check children's work.

Copy the words. **Write** the letters from left to right.

Nan   nap

man   tan

Nat   can

pan   mat

Home Activity Your child practiced writing words with *Nn*. Have your child find all the words above that have an *N* or *n* in them and practice writing them one more time.

Name _____

Trace the arrows.
Connect the word trains from left to right and top to bottom.

START:

END

Home Activity Your child learned that reading is done from top to bottom, and from left to right with a return sweep. Show your child a page from a favorite book. Have him or her tell you where to start reading a sentence (left) and in which direction to read (to the right). Remind your child that reading starts at the top and goes to the bottom of the page.

© Pearson Education, Inc., 1

Name _____

Say the word for each picture.
Write the letter on the line that begins the word.

1. p
2. c
3. c
4. n
5. p
6. n

Write p or **n** on the line to complete the word.

7. cap
8. pan
9. man
10. map

© Pearson Education, Inc., 1

School + Home **Home Activity** Your child reviewed words that begin with *c*, *n*, and *p* and reviewed words that end with *n* and *p*. Have your child find other words with /c/ as in *cat*, /p/ as in *pig*, and /n/ as in *nut*.

Name _____

Read the story.

Draw a picture that shows where the story takes place.

Mei and Jake walk in the warm sand.

Waves splash their bare feet.

Mei and Jake decide to make a sand castle.

They make thick walls and tall towers.

The children stand up to look at their castle.

Suddenly a giant wave comes to shore!

Now the castle is gone.

Drawing should be a beach that shows sand and waves.

© Pearson Education, Inc., 1

Home Activity Your child read a story (fiction) and then identified where the story takes place (setting). Have your child name one or two favorite stories. Help your child identify the setting of each story.

Name _____

Nouns: Places

Mark the noun for a place that completes the sentence.

1. We see animals at the _____.
   - ⊗ zoo
   - ○ fish
   - ○ eat

2. Sam and Tam swim in the _____.
   - ○ cat
   - ○ dip
   - ⊗ lake

3. Tip can run in the _____.
   - ⊗ park
   - ○ man
   - ○ pet

4. The _____ has a big yard.
   - ○ call
   - ○ baby
   - ⊗ home

© Pearson Education, Inc., 1

Home Activity Your child prepared for taking tests on nouns for places. Read a story together. Have your child point out the nouns that name places.

Name _____

Sam and His Cat Max
Contents

Chapter 1   Sam 3
Chapter 2   A New Pet for Sam 7
Chapter 3   Max the Cat 11
Chapter 4   Max Gets Big 15
Chapter 5   Sam's Fat Cat. 19

1. **Draw** a circle around the page numbers.

2. **Draw** a box around the chapter titles.

3. **Write** the name of Chapter 5.

Sam's Fat Cat

4. **Write** the page number on which "A New Pet for Sam" begins.

7

5. **Write** how many chapters are listed.

5

Home Activity Your child learned to use the table of contents in a book to find information. As you read together, point out the table of contents and encourage your child to help you find information such as the page number for a specific chapter.

Name _____

Snap!

Copy the words. Make sure you write your tall and small letters the correct size. Remember **p** falls below the line.

Nan   Nan

man   man

pan   pan

Sam   Sam

tan   tan

cat   cat

Pam   Pam

tap   tap

sat   sat

pat   pat

can   can

mat   mat

Mac   Mac

map   map

sap   sap

Cam   Cam

Ann   Ann

cap   cap

Home Activity Your child practiced writing words with *Aa, Mm, Ss, Tt, Cc, Pp,* and *Nn*. Have your child choose a word that begins with the letter *p* from the list and then write the word. Repeat for the letters *m, s, t, c,* and *n*.

© Pearson Education, Inc., 1

38 Handwriting

Name _____

Underline the name of the book.

Place an X over the book about Sam.

Circle the book that Nan wrote.
Draw a box around the book that Pam drew pictures for.

Home Activity Your child learned to use the information on a book cover and title page to figure out what the book is about. Point out the cover and title page of the next book you read together. Explain that the title tells what the book is about.

Name _____

Read the words in the box.
Pick a word to finish each sentence.
Write it on the line.

we   like   the   one

1. Here is _____**the**_____ man.

2. I _____**like**_____ to run with my .

3. I have _____**one**_____ too.

4. _____**We**_____ have a and a .

© Pearson Education, Inc., 1

School + Home **Home Activity** This week your child identified and read the words *we*, *like*, *the*, and *one*. Write each word on a card. Have your child read each word and then use it in a sentence.

Ff

Say the word for each picture.

Write f on the line if the word has the same first sound as .

1. _____
   ---**f**---
   _____

2. _____

   _____

3. _____
   ---**f**---
   _____

4. _____
   ---**f**---
   _____

5. _____

   _____

6. _____
   ---**f**---
   _____

7. _____

   _____

8. _____
   ---**f**---
   _____

© Pearson Education, Inc., 1

Home Activity Your child learned that some words begin with the letter *f*. Have your child find other words with /f/ as in *fish*.

Name _____

Look at the pictures.
Tell a story about the pictures.
Draw a picture to tell what happens next.

Check children's drawings.

Home Activity Your child learned that the plot tells what happens in a story. Have your child tell you a story about the pictures on this page. Help your child by asking what happens in the beginning of the story, in the middle, and at the end.

Name _____

Trace and **write** the letters. Make sure you write your letters the correct size.

F F

f f

Check children's work.

Copy the words. **Write** the letters the correct size.

Fam   Fam   fan   fan

pat   pat   sat   sat

Ann   Ann   fat   fat

nap   nap   man   man

Home Activity Your child practiced writing words with *Ff*. Have your child choose two words from above that begin with *f* and practice writing the words again.

© Pearson Education, Inc., 1

Name _____

Underline the name of the person who wrote the book.
Circle the name of the person who drew the pictures.

Sit Sam Sit

By <u>Dan Buck</u>

Drawings by
(Tim Mix)

Circle the book that Kim Fin wrote.

Sit Sam Sit

By Dan Buck

Drawings by
Tim Mix

Jam for Pam

By Kim Fin

Drawings by
Pat Kip

Place an X over the book about Tam.

Sam

by Tip

Tam

by Mat

Home Activity Your child learned to use the information on a book cover and title page to figure out what the book is about. Your child also learned to look for the name of the author and illustrator of a book. Discuss illustrations in a favorite book with your child.

Name _____

Bb

Say the word for each picture.

Write **b** on the line if the word has the same first sound as .

1. _____

2. __b__

3. __b__

4. __b__

5. __b__

6. _____

Write two words that rhyme with **nab**.

7. **t ab**

8. **c ab**

© Pearson Education, Inc., 1

Home Activity Your child learned that some words begin and end with the letter *b*. Have your child find other words with /b/ as in *balloon*.

Verbs

A **verb** names an action. It tells what a person or thing does.

The dog **eats. Eats** is the verb.

Circle the verb in each sentence.

1. Sam and Tip run in the yard.

2. The cat hit the bag.

3. They play with the bag.

4. The cat fit in a bag.

5. Tam hid in the bag.

Find other verbs. **Say** a sentence for each verb.

© Pearson Education, Inc., 1

School + Home **Home Activity** Your child learned about verbs. Have your child think of a verb and then pantomime the action.

Name _____

Trace and **write** the letters. Make sure you write your letters the correct size.

Copy the words. Sit and hold your paper the correct way.

Bab   nab

bat _____   ban

Tab   cab

bam _____   fat

Home Activity Your child practiced writing words with *Bb*. Have your child choose a word from above with *B* and a word with *b* and practice writing each three times as neatly as possible.

Name _____

Underline the title of the book.

Circle who wrote the book.

Circle the book that Peg Bud wrote.
Draw a box around the book that Ken Fox drew the pictures for.

© Pearson Education, Inc., 1

Home Activity Your child learned to use the information on a book cover and title page to figure out what the book is about. Your child also learned to look for the name of the author and illustrator of a book. On a book your child enjoys, point out the cover and title page. Point to the name of the author and read it aloud.

Name _____

Gg

Say the word for each picture.
Write g on the line if the word has the same first sound as .

1. **g**

2. **g**

3. _____

4. _____

Write four words that rhyme with **gag.**

5. **s ag**

6. **n ag**

7. **t ag**

8. **b ag**

Home Activity Your child has learned that some words begin and end with the letter g. Have your child find other words with /g/ as in *goat*. Work with your child to make words that rhyme with *gag*.

Name _____

Read the words in the box.
Pick a word to finish each sentence.
Write it on the line.

do   look   you   was   yellow

1. Tip ____**was**____ sad.

2. ____**Look**____ in the .

3. ____**Do**____ you see the ?

4. The is ____**yellow**____ .

5. ____**You**____ can hold the .

Home Activity This week your child identified and read the words *do, look, you, was,* and *yellow*. As you read with your child, encourage him or her to point out these words in print.

50 High-Frequency Words

© Pearson Education, Inc., 1

Name _____

Verbs

Tell about things you do in the yard.
Finish the sentences.
Use words from the box or your own words.

> ride a bike   run   play catch   jump rope

I Answers will vary. Possible answer: I ride my bike in the yard.   in the yard.

I Answers will vary. Possible answer: I jump rope in the yard.   in the yard.

I Answers will vary. Possible answer: I play catch in the yard.   in the yard.

Say a sentence to tell what you like to do.

© Pearson Education, Inc., 1

School + Home **Home Activity** Your child learned how to use verbs in writing. Have your child write two sentences that tell about what he or she does after school. Ask your child to identify the verbs in the sentences.

Name _____

Trace and **write** the letters. Make sure you write your letters the correct size.

 G   G

 g   g

Check children's work.

Copy the words.

Gam Gam   nag   nag

bag   bag   gas   gas

tag   tag   gab   gab

Did you write the letter g so that it falls below the line each time?

Yes   No

 Home Activity Your child practiced writing words with *Gg*. Say the following words: *Gus, Gary, Gwen, girl, give, get.* Have your child write *G* or *g* to show how each word begins.

Name _____

a b c d e f g h i j k l m n o p q r s t u v w x y z

Circle the letter that comes first in the alphabet.

I.

s t (a)

2.

(c) p n

3.

f (b) g

4.

n (a) g

5.

s (f) p

6.

t (g) n

Write the letters in alphabetical order.

7. m a s

a m s

8. t c p

c p t

9. n f b g

b f g n

10. t g n

g n t

II. s c f

c f s

12. n a p f

a f n p

© Pearson Education, Inc., 1

Home Activity Your child learned to put letters in alphabetical order. Write three different letters on index cards, one letter on each card. Have your child put the letters in alphabetical order.

Ii

Say the word for each picture.
Write i on the line if the word has the same first sound as .

Say the word for each picture.
Write i on the line if the word has the same middle sound as .

 Home Activity Your child learned that some words have the short i sound. Have your child find other words with /i/ at the beginning or in the middle, such as *ink* and *sit*.

© Pearson Education, Inc., 1

Name _____

Read the story.
Circle the picture that shows what happened next.

Maria put on her baseball uniform.

Dad helped Maria find her baseball cap.

Then Maria and Dad got in the car.

Dad drove to the baseball field.

Maria ran over to her team, the Hawks.

The coach told Maria to pick up a bat.

Home Activity Your child read a story and then identified the events that happen, or the plot, in the story. Read a fiction story with your child and have your child tell you the important events in the story.

Name _____

Verbs

Mark the sentence that has a line under the verb.

1. ○ Sam jumps in the <u>bag</u>.
   ⊗ Sam <u>jumps</u> in the bag.
   ○ <u>Sam</u> jumps in the bag.

2. ⊗ She can <u>tap</u> the bag.
   ○ She can tap the <u>bag</u>.
   ○ <u>She</u> can tap the bag.

3. ○ <u>She</u> can see the hat.
   ⊗ She can <u>see</u> the hat.
   ○ She can see the <u>hat</u>.

4. ○ He can play <u>here</u>.
   ○ He <u>can</u> play here.
   ⊗ He can <u>play</u> here.

School + Home   **Home Activity** Your child prepared for taking tests on verbs. Read a story together. Have your child point out the verbs in the story.

Name _____

Read each question. **Circle** the correct answer.

1. This sign tells you how fast to go.

2. This sign tells you not to go.

3. What does this sign mean?

   eat here   do not speed   stop

4. What does this sign mean?

   police   library   hospital

5. Which sign would help you if you were sick?

 Home Activity Your child learned the meanings of many different signs. Take a walk in the neighborhood and point out the different signs you see on the road or street. See how many of the signs your child can explain.

Name _____

Trace and **write** the letters. Make sure you write your letters the correct size.

I I

i i

Check children's work.

Copy the words. Write the tall and small letters the correct size. Write **p** and **g** so that they fall below the line.

If   If   sit   sit

pan   pan   tap   tap

pig   pig   big   big

School + Home

Home Activity Your child practiced writing words with *Ii*. Have your child think of words that rhyme with *pig*. Then help your child write two of the rhyming words: *big, dig, fig, rig, wig.*

58 Handwriting

a b c d e f g h i j k l m n o p q r s t u v w x y z

Circle the letter that comes first in the alphabet.

1.
s   t   (i)

2.
(a)   p   n

3.
f   (c)   g

4.
g   s   (f)

5.
n   (i)   p

6.
t   (g)   n

Write the letters in alphabetical order.

7. b a g

a b g

8. p c i

c i p

9. g f b

b f g

10. p a s

a p s

11. n c i

c i n

12. t f b

b f t

© Pearson Education, Inc., 1

Home Activity Your child learned to put letters in alphabetical order. Write three different letters on index cards, one letter on each card. Have your child put the letters in alphabetical order, and then write them in order.

Name _____

Read the words in the box.
Pick a word to finish each sentence.
Write it on the line.

do   look   you   was   yellow

1. This is __**yellow**__ .

2. Can __**you**__ see the ?

3. __**Look**__ at that big !

4. The __**was**__ in the bag!

5. __**Do**__ you like my ?

 Home Activity This week your child learned to read the words *do, look, you, was,* and *yellow*. Write each word on a card. Have your child read each word and then use it in a sentence.

Name _____

Dd

Say the word for each picture.

Write **d** on the line if the word has the same first sound as .

Say the word for each picture.

Write **d** on the line if the word has the same ending sound as .

Home Activity Your child learned that some words begin and end with the letter *d*. Have your child find other words that begin and end with /d/.

Name _____

Circle the make-believe pictures.
Draw a box around the real pictures.

1.

2.

3.

4.

5.

6.

Home Activity Your child looked at pictures to tell which may be real and which may be make-believe. Have your child draw a picture of something that is make-believe and then draw a picture of something that is real.

© Pearson Education, Inc., 1

Name _____

Trace and write the letters. Make sure you write your letters the correct size.

<u>Check children's work.</u>

Copy the words. Write the letters the correct size.

Dan   fad

Dad   bad

dip   pad

dig   Sid

 Home Activity Your child practiced writing words with *Dd*. Have your child choose a word from above with *D* and a word with *d* and then write the words as neatly as possible.

© Pearson Education, Inc., 1

Name _____

Circle the title of the book.
Underline the author of the book.
Draw a box around the illustrator of the book.

Three Pups

By <u>Sue Green</u>

Illustrated by
Mick Bell

Circle the book that Bess Dell wrote.
Draw a box around the book that Tom Lock illustrated.

Nuts

By Bess Dell

Illustrated by
Ron Ness

Fog

By Rex Dab

Illustrated by
Tom Lock

Home Activity Your child learned to use the information on a book cover and title page to figure out what the book is about. Your child also learned to look for the name of the author and illustrator of a book. On a book your child enjoys, point out the cover and title page. Point to the name of the illustrator and read it aloud. Discuss the illustrations and invite your child to express an opinion about the illustrator.

L l

Say the word for each picture.

Write l on the line if the word has the same first sound as _____ .

1.	2. l
3. l	4. l
5.	6. l

Write two words that rhyme with **pill**.

Possible answers are shown.

7. **mill, fill**   8. **bill, sill**

Home Activity Your child learned that some words begin with the letter *l*. Have your child find other words with /l/ as in *ladder*.

Simple Sentences

A **sentence** has a noun and a verb. It tells who did what.

The **dog jumps**.

    Dog is a noun.

    Jumps is a verb.

Find the sentence. **Circle** the sentence.

1. The cat can run by Tam.

    run by Tam

2. got the top

    She got the top.

3. The doll is on the mat.

    the doll

4. The cat sat on the mat.

    the mat

© Pearson Education, Inc., 1

Home Activity Your child learned about simple sentences. Have your child find things in your house to make sentences about. Have your child identify the parts of his or her sentences.

Name _____

Trace and **write** the letters. Make sure you write your letters the correct size.

Check children's work.

Copy the words. Sit and hold your paper the correct way.

Lin

Cal

lid

lad

pill

lip

lab

mill

© Pearson Education, Inc., 1

Home Activity Your child practiced writing *Ll*. Say names and words that begin with *L* or *l* and have your child write the correct letter each time you say a name or word.

Name _____

a b c d e f g h i j k l m n o p q r s t u v w x y z

Circle the letter that comes first in the alphabet.

I.	2.	3.
(a) l t	(i) p n	f (d) g

4.	5.	6.
t (h) l	s (n) p	d (c) g

Write the letters in alphabetical order.

7. m b s	8. t d p	9. t f b
b m s	**d p t**	**b f t**

10. p w n	11. f c i	12. i f b g
n p w	**c f i**	**b f g i**

© Pearson Education, Inc., 1

Home Activity Your child learned to sequence the letters of the alphabet. Write three different letters in random order. Have your child write the letters in alphabetical order.

Name _____

Hh

Say the word for each picture.
Write h on the line if the word has the same first sound as .

1. _____ h _____

2. _____ h _____

3. _____ _____

4. _____ _____

5. _____ h _____

6. _____ h _____

7. _____ _____

8. _____ h _____

© Pearson Education, Inc., 1

School + Home **Home Activity** Your child learned that some words begin with the letter *h*. Have your child find other words with /h/ as in *helicopter*.

Phonics Consonant *Hh/h/* **69**

Name _____

Read the words in the box.
Pick a word to finish each sentence.
Write it on the line. **Remember** to begin a sentence with a capital letter.

| are | have | they | that | two |

1. _____**They**_____ are playing in the .

2. Look at _____**that**_____ white .

3. We _____**have**_____ a little .

4. My _____**two**_____ went home.

5. There _____**are**_____ three .

Home Activity This week your child identified and read the words *are, have, they, that,* and *two.* As you read with your child, encourage him or her to point out these words in print.

Name _____

Simple Sentences

Tell a story about what you like to play with.
Finish the sentence. **Use** words from the box.
Write a sentence of your own.

> a doll   a ball   a toy car   games   a top

I like to play with _____ .

I like to play with _____ .

Answers will vary. Possible answer: I like to play with a doll. I like
to play with games. I play in my room.

_____

_____

Say other sentences using the toys.

Home Activity Your child learned how to use simple sentences in writing. Have your child write two
sentences that tell how he or she can help clean up a mess.

© Pearson Education, Inc., 1

Name _____

Trace and **write** the letters. Make sure you write your letters the correct size.

_____

- -

_____

_____

<u>**Check children's work.**</u>

Copy the words.

Halt   his

Han   hat

hip   hand

Did you remember the crossbar on the letter **H**? | **Yes** | **No**

 Home Activity Your child practiced writing words with *Hh*. Say the following words: *Hal, Hank, Harry, have, him, hit.* Have your child write *H* or *h* to show how each word begins.

© Pearson Education, Inc., 1

Name _____

a b c d e f g h i j k l m n o p q r s t u v w x y z

Circle the letter that comes first in the alphabet.

1. i t (h)

2. (d) p n

3. s (b) g

4. t (f) m

5. s (p) t

6. n (g) l

Write the letters in alphabetical order.

7. b d g

b d g

8. n f l

f l n

9. c b p

b c p

10. v h s

h s v

11. m f o

f m o

12. t m b i

b i m t

© Pearson Education, Inc., 1

School + Home

Home Activity Your child learned to put words in alphabetical order. Say two different letters in random order. Have your child write the letters in alphabetical order.

Name _____

Oo

Say the word for each picture.
Write o on the line if the word has the same first sound as .

1. **o**	2. _____
3. _____	4. **o**

Say the word for each picture.
Write o on the line if the word has the same middle sound as ●.

5. **top**

6. **doll**

7. **p n**

8. **mop**

School + Home

Home Activity Your child learned about the short o vowel sound in words. Have your child find other words with /o/ at the beginning or in the middle, such as *octopus* and *box*.

Name _____

Read the story. **Circle** the make-believe pictures.
Draw a box around the real pictures.

My friend lives on a farm.

I like to visit the farm.

I help my friend feed the chickens.

We let the cows out of the barn.

One day we pick corn.

There is a lot of work to do on a farm.

1.

2.

3.

4.

5.

6.

© Pearson Education, Inc., 1

School + Home **Home Activity** Your child read a story and then identified pictures of real things and make-believe things. Remind your child that some stories could really happen and some stories are make believe. Have your child draw a picture of a real pig and a make-believe pig.

Genre/Literary Analysis 75

Name _____

Simple Sentences

Mark the group of words that is a sentence.

1. ○ look at that green
   ○ that green top
   ⊗ Look at that green top.

2. ⊗ The dog will jump.
   ○ will jump
   ○ the dog

3. ○ cat can do
   ○ look what the cat
   ⊗ Look what the cat can do.

4. ○ Mom can see the
   ⊗ Mom can see the bag.
   ○ the bag

© Pearson Education, Inc., 1

School + Home

Home Activity Your child prepared for taking tests on simple sentences. Read a story together. Have your child point out the parts of the sentences.

Name _____

Circle the traffic symbols in each row.

1.

2.

Place an X on the symbols that are found on the map.

3.

Home Activity Your child has learned to identify traffic and map symbols. Point out traffic symbols when on the road together. Point out map symbols when you look at maps together.

Name _____

Trace and **write** the letters. Make sure you write your letters the correct size.

Check children's work.

Copy the words. **Write** the tall and small letters the correct size. Write **p** and **g** so that they fall below the line.

On   On   golf   golf

dog   dog   hog   hog

pot   pot   hop   hop

Home Activity Your child practiced writing *Oo*. Say names and words that begin with *O* (*Otto, Oscar, Otis*) and *o* (*only, octopus, ostrich, olive*) and have your child write the correct letter each time you say a name or word.

School + Home

© Pearson Education, Inc., 1

Name _____

a b c d e f g h i j k l m n o p q r s t u v w x y z

Circle the letter that comes first in the alphabet.

1. o t (d)

2. (i) p n

3. s (f) l

4. g s (f)

5. s (o) p

6. t (h) n

Write the letters in alphabetical order.

7. p o l t

l o p t

8. t b i a

a b i t

9. r h v a

a h r v

10. m u s z

m s u z

11. g j d c

c d g j

12. s n a o

a n o s

Home Activity Your child learned to put words in alphabetical order. Say three different letters in random order. Have your child write the letters in alphabetical order.

Name _____

Read the words in the box.
Pick a word to finish each sentence.
Write it on the line.

are   have   they   that   two

1. I like _____ **that** _____ pretty .

2. The _____ **are** _____ all black.

3. Stella has _____ **two** _____ big .

4. Jan and Pete _____ **have** _____ funny .

5. When will _____ **they** _____ go to the ?

© Pearson Education, Inc., 1

Home Activity This week your child identified and read the words *are, have, they, that,* and *two.* As you read with your child, encourage him or her to point out these words in print.

Name _____

Rr

Say the word for each picture.
Write r on the line if the word has the same first sound as .

1. _____

2. ___ **r** ___

3. ___ **r** ___

4. ___ **r** ___

5. _____

6. ___ **r** ___

7. _____

8. ___ **r** ___

© Pearson Education, Inc., 1

Home Activity Your child learned that some words begin with the letter *r*. Have your child find other words that begin with /r/ as in *rocket*.

Name _____

Look at the pictures.

Circle the picture to show what happens next.

Look at the pictures.
Draw a picture of what could happen next.

Children's artwork should show something that a boy or a girl might do in school.

Home Activity Your child has learned to identify plot, or the events that happen, in a story. When you read a story with your child, have your child retell the important events in the story.

Name _____

Trace and **write** the letters. Make sure you write your letters the correct size.

R R R

r r r

Check children's work.

Copy the words. Write the letters the correct size.

Rob   Rob

rat

Ron   Ron

rod

ran   ran

rib   rib

rip   rip

rig

© Pearson Education, Inc., 1

Home Activity Your child practiced writing words with *Rr*. Have your child choose one word with *R* and one word with *r* from above, and practice writing the words one more time.

Name _____

Circle the title of the book.
Underline the author of the book.
Draw a box around the illustrator of the book.

How
to Care
for Pets

By Don Lund

Illustrated by
Jen Lint

Contents

Dogs 3
Cats 10
Fish 18
Birds 24
Rats 36

---

1. **Draw** a circle around the page numbers.

2. **Put** a box around the chapter titles.

3. **Write** the page number where the chapter about fish begins.

_____
18
_____

© Pearson Education, Inc., 1

Home Activity Your child learned to use the title, author's name, illustrator's name and the table of contents in a nonfiction book to find information. As you read together, point out the table of contents send encourage your child to help you find information such as the page number for a specific chapter.

Name _____

Jj   Ww

Say the word for each picture.
Write j on the line if the word has the same first sound as .
Write w on the line if the word has the same first sound as [waterfall] .

1. _____ **W** _____

2. _____

3. _____

4. _____ **W**

5. _____ **j**

6. _____ **j**

7. _____

8. _____ **W**

Home Activity Your child learned that some words begin with the letter *w* and some words begin with the letter *j*. Have your child find other words that begin with /w/ as in *waterfall* and /j/ as in *jet*.

Phonics Consonants *Ww*/w/ and *Jj*/j/   **85**

© Pearson Education, Inc., 1

Name _____

Adjectives

An **adjective** tells about a person, place, or thing.

a **big** book

Read the sentence.
Circle the adjective.

1. Sam sees the (yellow) bus.

2. Sam has a (big) bag.

3. He met (fun) friends.

4. We read (new) books.

5. Jill can play with the (red) ball.

Say each word you circled in a sentence.

Home Activity Your child learned about adjectives. Have your child choose objects from home and use an adjective to describe each one.

© Pearson Education, Inc., 1

Name _____

Trace and **write** the letters.
Make sure you write your letters
the correct size.

 W   W   W

_____

Check children's work.

 W   W

J   J   J

 j   j   j

 Home Activity Your child practiced writing letters *Ww* and *Jj*. Have your child practice writing all four letters three more times. Make sure he or she writes the *j* so that it has a dot above it and falls below the line.

Handwriting 87

Name _____

Circle the title of the book.
Underline the author of the book.
Draw a box around the illustrator of the book.

Ant Jobs

By Pat Lund

Illustrated by
Gus Kit

Contents

Ants That Lay Eggs. 3
Ants That Are Dads 10
Ants That Dig 16
Ants That Find Food 24
Ants That Plant Food 36

---

1. **Draw** a circle around the page numbers.

2. **Put** a box around the chapter titles.

3. **Write** the page number where the chapter about Ants That

Dig begins. _____ **16** _____

© Pearson Education, Inc., 1

Home Activity Your child learned to use the title, author's name, illustrator's name and the table of contents in a nonfiction book to find information. Point out the information on the cover and the table of contents in an interesting book. Encourage your child to count the number of chapters, find the page number for a specific chapter, and turn to that page.

School + Home

Kk

Name _____

Say the word for each picture.
Write k on the line if the word has the same first sound as .

1. _____

2. ___ **k** ___

3. ___ **k** ___

4. _____

5. ___ **k** ___

6. _____

Pick a word to finish each sentence.
Write the word on the line.

Kim   kiss   kit

7. Sam will ___ **kiss** ___ Mom.

8. ___ **Kim** ___ will hit the rim with the ⬤ .

Home Activity Your child learned that some words begin with the letter *k*. Have your child find other words that begin with /k/ as in *kitten*.

Name _____

Read the words in the box.
Pick a word to finish each sentence.
Write it on the line. **Remember** to begin each sentence with a capital letter.

he   is   to   with   three

1. She ___**is**___ on the .

2. Bill came ___**to**___ .

3. We have ___**three**___ books.

 4. My ___ are ___**with**___ me.

5. ___**He**___ has a cat.

 Home Activity This week your child identified and read the words *he, is, to, with,* and *three.* As you read with your child, encourage him or her to point out these words in print.

Name _____

Adjectives

Tell about your room at school.
Finish the sentences. **Use** words from the box.
Write a sentence of your own.

| big | small | nice | new |

The room is _____ ~~Answers will vary. Possible answer: The room is big.~~ ~~The room is nice.~~ _____.

The room is _____.

_____

_____

_____

_____

Say other sentences using the adjectives in the box.

© Pearson Education, Inc., 1

School + Home

Home Activity Your child learned how to use adjectives in writing. Have your child write two sentences that describe his or her favorite toy. Ask your child to identify the adjectives in the sentences.

Name _____

School Day

Name _____

Trace and **write** the letters. Make sure you write your letters the correct size.

Check children's work.

Copy the words.

Kip   kid

tack   sock

kiss   Kim

Did you write each **K** and **k** the correct size? | **Yes** | **No** |

 Home Activity Your child practiced writing words with *Kk*. Say the following words: *Kim, Karen, Kevin, kite, kitchen, kitten.* Have your child write *K* or *k* to show how each word begins.

© Pearson Education, Inc., 1

92 Handwriting

Name _____

a b c d e f g h i j k l m n o p q r s t u v w x y z

Circle the letter that comes first in the alphabet.

1. w j (e)

2. k (i) r

3. s (c) l

4. o n (h)

5. (f) n m

6. p (d) g

Write the letters in alphabetical order.

7. y p e s

e p s y

8. g i f a

a f g i

9. t x m b

b m t x

10. q o m r

m o q r

11. t n l o

l n o t

12. e a d b

a b d e

Home Activity Your child learned to sequence letters of the alphabet. Say four different letters in random order. Have your child write the letters in alphabetical order. Then give your child five letter cards and have him or her put them in alphabetical order.

Name _____

Ee

Say the word for each picture.

Write **e** on the line if the word has the same first sound as .

1. _____ **e** _____

2. _____ _____

3. _____ **e** _____

4. _____ _____

Say the word for each picture.

Write **e** on the line if the word has the same middle sound as .

5. _____ **e** _____

6. _____ _____

7. _____ **e** _____

8. _____ **e** _____

Home Activity Your child learned that some words have the short *e* sound. Have your child find other words with /e/ at the beginning or in the middle, such as *elephant* and *bell*.

Name _____

Read the story.

Write 1, 2, 3 on the lines to tell what happens in the beginning, middle,

Lucy plays outside with her puppy.

She wears a big, straw sunhat.

The wind blows the hat off Lucy's head.

So Mom sews ribbons to the hat.

Mom ties the ribbons under Lucy's chin.

Now Lucy's hat stays on.

3

1

2

 Home Activity Your child read a story and then identified the order of events that happen in a story. This story has a problem and solution. Reread the story with your child. Have your child tell you the problem in the story and how the problem is solved.

Genre/Literary Analysis **95**

Name _____

Adjectives

Mark the sentence that has a line under the adjective.

1. ⊗ Sam can hop on the <u>big</u> bus.
   ○ <u>Sam</u> can hop on the big bus.
   ○ Sam can <u>hop</u> on the big bus.

2. ○ <u>She</u> is a happy girl.
   ○ She is a happy <u>girl</u>.
   ⊗ She is a <u>happy</u> girl.

3. ○ We can read a short <u>book</u>.
   ⊗ We can read a <u>short</u> book.
   ○ We can <u>read</u> a short book.

4. ⊗ She will eat <u>hot</u> food.
   ○ <u>She</u> will eat hot food.
   ○ She will eat hot <u>food</u>.

Choose other adjectives. **Say** a sentence for each adjective.

© Pearson Education, Inc., 1

Home Activity Your child prepared for taking tests on adjectives. Read a story together. Have your child identify the adjectives in the story.

Name _____

Look at the calendar. **Read** the questions.
Circle the answers.

1. What day comes after Monday?

Sunday   (Tuesday)   Thursday

2. What day comes after Thursday?

Wednesday   Saturday   (Friday)

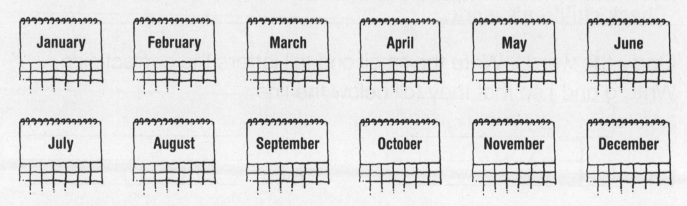

3. What month comes after March?

(April)   May   December

4. What month comes after June?

August   (July)   October

Home Activity Your child has learned how a calendar shows the order of the days and months. Look at calendars with your child. Have him or her point out the order of the days, weeks, and months.

Name _____

Trace and **write** the letters. Make sure you write your letters the correct size.

E   E   E

e   e   e

Check children's work.

Copy the words. Write the small and tall letters the correct size. Write **g** and **j** so that they fall below the line.

Ed   Ed   men   men

get   get   egg   egg

jet   jet   beg   beg

Home Activity Your child practiced writing words with *Ee*. Have your child copy the sentence and draw a picture to fill in the blank: *Ed has a pet_____.*

School + Home

Name _____

Read each group of words.
Circle the group of words that is a sentence.

1. sat fat the a is

   (Sam can see a cat.)

   Sam a mad is I

2. (The cat is fat.)

   cat Tam is the

   Snap tap cat the

3. He cat the on bat

   (He is on the mat.)

   mat cat is in nap

4. (Tip is with Tam.)

   cat see Tip can

   Tam is hat mat

5. Egg hen the with is this

   egg the with is this hen.

   (The hen is with this egg.)

6. egg chick a is in the

   (A chick is in the egg.)

   chick A egg in is the

School + Home

Home Activity Your child learned to recognize sentences. Write groups of simple words that are sentences and groups of words that are not. Ask your child to identify the sentences and explain his or her choices.

Print Awareness 99

Name _____

Read the words in the box.
Pick a word to finish each sentence.
Write it on the line.

| he | is | to | with | three |

1. Basketball _____**is**_____ fun.

2. The _____**three**_____ squirrels are eating .

3. Sam likes to play _____**with**_____ Pat.

4. We can go _____**to**_____ the party Saturday.

5. When will _____**he**_____ move to his new house?

Home Activity This week your child identified and read the words *he, is, to, with,* and *three*. As you read with your child, encourage him or her to point out these words in print.

Vv

Say the word for each picture.
Write v on the line if the word has the same first sound as .

1. _____ **v**

2. _____ _____

3. _____ _____

4. _____ **V**

5. _____ **V**

6. _____ **V**

Write V or **v** to make a word.

7. **vat**

8. **Vic**

9. **Val**

10. **van**

Home Activity Your child learned that some words begin with the letter *v*. Have your child find other words with /v/ as in *volcano*.

Name _____

Circle the make-believe pictures.
Draw a box around the real pictures.

1.

2.

3.

4.

5.

6.

© Pearson Education, Inc., 1

School + Home

Home Activity Your child looked at pictures to tell which may be real and which may be make-believe. With your child, look at a book about how real people and animals live.

Name _____

Trace and **write** the letters. Make sure you write your letters the correct size.

Check children's work.

Copy the words. Write the letters the correct size.

Val   vent

Vin   vat

vest   van

vast   Vic

Home Activity Your child practiced writing words with *Vv*. Have your child choose a word that begins with *V* and a word that begins with *v* from above, and practice writing each word two more times.

© Pearson Education, Inc., 1

Name _____

Read each group of words.
Find and **copy** the complete sentence.

1. The cat ran.
   is my hat
   had been to

   The cat ran.

2. Kim can win.
   run Kim to see
   my van is a

   Kim can win.

3. A big jet is.
   Pam can pat the cat.
   on mat we see cat on

   Pam can pat the cat.

4. My top is in
   The lad is sad.
   Is sad the lad

   The lad is sad.

© Pearson Education, Inc., 1

Home Activity Your child learned to recognize sentences and features such as capitalization and end punctuation. Have your child circle the capital letter in each sentence on this page.

Name _____

Yy   Zz

Say the word for each picture.
Write y on the line if the word has the same first sound as .
Write z on the line if the word has the same first sound as [zebra] .

1.	z	2.	
3.	z	4.	y
5.		6.	y
7.	z	8.	y

Home Activity Your child learned that some words begin with *y* and some words begin with *z*. Have your child find other words that begin with /y/ as in *yo-yo* and /z/ as in *zebra*.

Phonics Consonant *Yy*/y/ and *Zz*/z/   **105**

© Pearson Education, Inc., 1

Name _____

Sentences

A **sentence** tells a complete idea.
It begins with a capital letter.
Many sentences end with a period.

noun

↑

The wet dog runs.

↓   ↓

adjective   verb

Find the sentence.

Underline the sentence.

1. <u>The girl will get the one with fuzz.</u>

   the one with fuzz

2. the fun park

   <u>They can go to the fun park.</u>

3. <u>Here is where they sell good fruit.</u>

   good fruit

4. wet up here

   <u>You can get wet up here.</u>

5. <u>I can see the big rainbow.</u>

   big rainbow

School + Home **Home Activity** Your child learned about expanding sentences. Say a simple sentence to your child and have him or her add a word to the sentence.

Name _____

Trace and **write** the letters.
Make sure you write your letters
the correct size.

Check children's work.

Home Activity Your child practiced writing *Yy* and *Zz*. Have your child practice writing all four letters three more times each.

Name _____

Read each group of words.
Find and **copy** the complete sentence.

1. pup Ned is a
   Ned and Ted
   Ned is a pup.

   Ned is a pup.

2. a is dog this
   This dog is a
   This is a dog.

   This is a dog.

3. Tim dog is for this
   This dog is for Tim.
   dog this Tim for is

   This dog is for Tim.

4. The dog nap and will Tim
   The dog and Tim nap.
   Tim nap dog The and will

   The dog and Tim nap.

Home Activity Your child learned to recognize sentences and features such as end punctuation. Find sentences and other groups of words in a flyer, periodical, or used worksheet. Ask your child to identify the sentences and circle the end punctuation.

© Pearson Education, Inc., 1

Uu

Say the name of the picture.
Write u on the line if the word has the same first sound as

1. u

2. _____

3. _____

4. u

Say the name of the picture.
Write u on the line if the word has the same middle sound as .

5. s u n

6. t u b

7. b u g

8. p _ n

© Pearson Education, Inc., 1

 School + Home **Home Activity** Your child learned about the short *u* vowel sound in words. Have your child find other words that have the same sound as /u/ at the beginning or in the middle, such as *umbrella* and *rug*.

Name _____

Read the words in the box.
Pick a word to finish each sentence. **Write** it on the line.
Remember to begin a sentence with a capital letter.

where   he   for   me   go

1. The ⬭ is for **me** .

2. We are waiting **for** the rain to stop.

3. **Where** can we buy pickles?

4. Let's **go** to the Farmers Market.

5. **He** had three yams.

© Pearson Education, Inc., 1

Home Activity This week your child identified and read the words *where, he, for, me,* and *go.* As you read with your child, encourage him or her to point out these words in print.

Name _____

Sentences

Tell about what you get at a store.
Use words from the box or words of your own.

> food   toys   books   games

Answers will vary. Possible answer: I get food at the store. I like to get toys. I have fun at the store.

Say other sentences about things in a store.

Home Activity Your child learned how to expand sentences in writing. Have your child add adjectives to the sentences he or she wrote.

Name _____

Trace and **write** the letters. Make sure you write your letters the correct size.

 U U

u u u

 u u

Check children's work.

Copy the words.

Uncle Uncle   junk junk

just just   dull dull

hug hug   sun sun

Did you write each **U** and **u** the correct size?   Yes   No

 School + Home **Home Activity** Your child practiced writing words with *Uu*. Read the following sentence to your child: *It is fun to run in the sun.* Have your child copy the sentence as neatly as he or she can.

Name _____

Read each group of words.
Find and **copy** the complete sentence.

1. pup sit and Tom
   The pup can sit.
   Tom the pup sit

2. A pup can run.
   The fat pup fat on
   fat pup beg can

The pup can sit. | A pup can run.

Finish each sentence. **Write** a word and a [.]

3. I like _____ Check children's words. Sentences should make sense. Make sure children end each sentence with a period. _____

4. We see a _____

5. Tom fed the _____

6. Sam is with _____

7. Tam can go _____

8. Tip has a yellow _____

Home Activity Your child learned to recognize sentences and features such as capitalization and end punctuation, and then use these features to complete sentences. Point to sentences in a newspaper or magazine. Have your child identify the features of a sentence. Then have your child find complete sentences.

© Pearson Education, Inc., 1

Name _____

Qq

Say the word for each picture.
Write **q** on the line if the word has the same first sound as .

1. **q**	2.
3. **q**	4.
5. **q**	6.

Write **qu** to make a word.

7. **quilt**   8. **quit**

9. **quiz**   10. **quick**

Home Activity Your child learned that some words begin with the letter *q*. Have your child find other words that begin with /kw/ as in *quilt*.

© Pearson Education, Inc., 1

Name _____

Read the story.
Look at each pair of pictures.
Circle the one that shows something real.

My class went to a museum.

Butterflies were flying around in a special room.

In another room, we learned about horses.

There were models and pictures of horses.

We saw the bones of a huge dinosaur.

That was my favorite part of the museum.

1.

2.

3.

4.

5.

6.

© Pearson Education, Inc., 1

Home Activity Your child read a story that could really happen. Then your child identified which of two pictures shows something real. Talk about a place you and your child have gone to, such as a zoo, park, or fair. Have your child name things that were real at that place.

Genre/Literary Analysis 115

Name _____

Sentences

Mark the word that completes the sentence.

1. Zak can _____ a big yam.
   - ○ girl
   - ○ fuzz
   - ⊗ sell

2. We go for a _____ run.
   - ○ Sam
   - ⊗ long
   - ○ quit

3. They can go here to get _____.
   - ○ mop
   - ○ run
   - ⊗ fruit

4. They can _____ up at the rainbow.
   - ⊗ look
   - ○ big
   - ○ zoo

School + Home **Home Activity** Your child prepared for taking tests on expanding sentences. Name a family member and have your child say two sentences about that person. Tell your child to include a noun, a verb, and an adjective in each sentence.

Name _____

1. **Circle** the shelf with .

2. **Draw** a box around the shelf with 📚 .

3. **Draw** an X over the computer.

4. **Draw** an arrow to the shelf with books of poems.

5. **Underline** the shelf with DVDs.

© Pearson Education, Inc., 1

Home Activity Your child learned to find resources in the library. Visit your local library with your child and help him or her find the storybooks, poems, newspapers, signs, and labels.

Name _____

Trace and **write** the letters.
Make sure you write your letters
the correct size.

_____

Check children's work.

_____

© Pearson Education, Inc., 1

School + Home **Home Activity** Your child practiced writing *Qu* and *qu*. Have your child practice writing this sentence: *Quin quit his quest.*

118 **Handwriting**

Name _____

Read each group of words.
Find and **copy** the complete sentence.

1. ham the Ben is for
    The ham is for Ben.
    Ben ham is the for

2. I see a big yam.
    A yam I see big
    See yam big I a

_____ | _____

The ham is for Ben. | **I see a big yam.**

Finish each sentence. **Write** a word and a [.]

3. Dad can **Check children's words. Sentences should make sense. Make sure children end each sentence with a period.**
_____

4. The hat is _____

5. They have to _____

6. A cat is on _____

7. Kit and Tip see _____

8. I see a green _____

Home Activity Your child learned to recognize sentences and features such as capitalization and end punctuation, and then use these features to complete sentences. Read the sentences that your child completed. Discuss the features of each sentence. Ask if each sentence makes sense.

Name _____

Read the words in the box.
Pick a word to finish each sentence.
Write it on the line.

where	he	for	me	go

1. Viv asked Tim if **he** could come to visit.

2. The rainbow may **go** away.

3. I know **where** you live.

4. Bill can come with **me** to the game.

5. She bought vegetables **for** Jan.

Home Activity This week your child identified and read the words *where, he, for, me,* and *go.* As you read with your child, encourage him or her to point out these words in print.

© Pearson Education, Inc., 1

Name _____

Say the word for each picture.
Write a on the line if you hear the **short a** sound.

c<u>a</u>t

I. _____
b **a** g

2. _____
f **a** n

3. _____
m ____ p

4. _____
m **a** p

---

5. _____
c **a** n

6. _____
m **a** n

7. _____
p ____ g

8. _____
v **a** n

Write a word for each picture.

9.

----- **bat** -----

10.

----- **hat** -----

Home Activity Your child has reviewed words with the short *a* sound heard in *cat*. Work with your child to make words that rhyme with *cat* and *man*.

Name _____

Read the words in the box.
Pick a word to finish each sentence.
Write it on the line.

my   on   way   in   come

1. We go that _____ **way** _____ to the .

2. The can _____ **come** _____ to me.

3. This is _____ **my** _____ .

4. The is _____ **on** _____ my .

5. The is _____ **in** _____ my .

Home Activity This week your child identified and read the words *in, on, my, way,* and *come*. Write each word on a card. Have your child read each word and then use it in a sentence.

122   High-Frequency Words

© Pearson Education, Inc., 1

Name _____

Look at the pictures.

Circle a word to finish each sentence of the story.

1. Sam has a cat.
   The cat had a ____.   (nap)   tag

2. The cat ran.
   Sam is ____.   lap   (sad)

3. The cat is in the jam.
   Sam is ____.   bad   (mad)

4. The cat ran.
   The cat is ____.   (bad)   sad

_____

Circle the picture to finish the sentence.

5. The story takes place in a ____.

Home Activity Your child identified characters' actions and feelings. Reread the story with your child. Talk about why Sam felt the way he did.

Comprehension Character and Setting **123**

Name _____

 Pooky the Cat

Pooky is our cat. He is silly. He plays with everything.

Today, Mom dropped a pen. The pen fell on the floor.

Pooky ran to the pen. He hit the pen. The pen rolled across

the floor. Pooky chased the pen. He hit it again. It rolled away.

"Silly Pooky!" said Mom. "He thinks the pen is a toy!"

Key Features of a Story

• The story has characters and tells what they do.

• It is made of sentences.

Name _____

Say the word for each picture.
Write ck on the line if the word has the same ending sound as .

1.	2.	3.	4.
ta **ck**	ba **ck**	fa _____	sa **ck**

5.	6.	7.	8.
ha _____	ja **ck**	pa **ck**	ca _____

Write two words that have the same ending sound as .

_____   _____

_____   _____

Home Activity Your child practiced reading and creating words that end in *ck*. Help your child write words that rhyme with *sack*.

Name _____

Short *a* Words

Write two list words that rhyme with **pan**.

1. **can**   2. **ran**

Write two list words that rhyme with **sad**.

3. **mad**   4. **dad**

Write two list words that rhyme with **tack**.

5. **back**   6. **sack**

Write two list words that rhyme with **hat**.

7. **cat**   8. **bat**

Write the missing words.   (am   at)

9. Look **at** _____ me.   10. I **am** _____ on a box.

Spelling Words
at
can
cat
back
dad
am
bat
mad
ran
sack

© Pearson Education, Inc., 1

Home Activity Your child wrote words with the short *a* vowel sound. Point to a picture on this page and have your child spell the word.

Name _____

Sentences

A **sentence** is a group of words that tells a complete idea. It begins with a capital letter. Many sentences end with a period (.).

The cat is on a mat.   ←   This is a sentence.
on a mat   ←   This is not a sentence.

Find the sentence. **Write** the sentence.

1. Jim has a pet.   has a pet

Jim has a pet.

2. His pet   His pet is a cat.

His pet is a cat.

3. The cat   The cat runs away.

The cat runs away.

4. Jim looks for his pet.   for his pet

Jim looks for his pet.

5. with Jim   We go with Jim.

We go with Jim.

Home Activity Your child learned about sentences. Name an animal your child knows. Have your child say two sentences about the animal.

Name _____

Story Chart

Title _____

Characters

Beginning

Middle

End of Story

Home Activity Your child is learning to write a little story. Ask your child what stories are like.

Name _____

_____
A

_____
a

Copy the words. Write the letters the correct size.

Ann Ann

nap nap

tap tap

ham ham

cap cap

ran ran

jab jab

yak yak

wag wag

sad sad

rag rag

pal pal

sat sat

Pam Pam

Did you write all of your letters the correct size?   Yes   No

Home Activity Your child practiced writing words with *A* and *a* and the short *a* sound. Have your child draw a picture of two of the words he or she wrote and label the pictures with the words.

© Pearson Education, Inc., 1

Name _____

Read each question. **Write** the correct answer.

a frog   (a bird)   a fish

1. Who is Ted? **a bird**

(in a nest)   on the ground   in a chair

2. Where does Ted sleep? **in a nest**

3. Which book is about pet doctors?

A Vet for My Pet

4. Which book could help you learn about feeding your pet?

Best Foods for Cats and Dogs

5. Which book would you choose to know more about birds?

A New Bed for Ted

 Home Activity Your child learned how to select books based on their titles or key words. Together with your child, make a list of topics you may enjoy reading about. Then, if possible, go to the library and choose some age-appropriate books based on your topics of interest.

© Pearson Education, Inc., 1

Jack and Dad Pack

Short a		Final –ck	High-Frequency Words
at	cap	ran	Jack	I
bag	Dad	sat	back	said
and	had	van	sack	the
bat	hat		pack	look
can	map			

Jack and Dad sat.

"I can pack the bag," said Dad.

"I can pack the sack," said Jack.

Dad had the bag at the van.

Jack ran back!

4

Decodable Story *Jack and Dad Pack*
Target Skill Short a, Final -ck

"I can pack the map," said Dad.

"I can pack the hat."

2

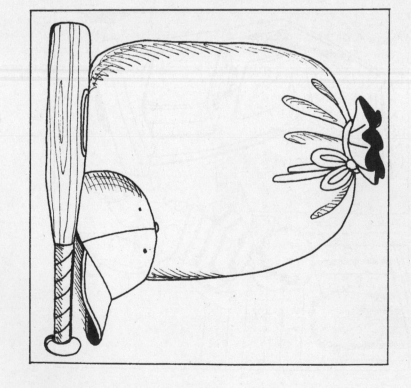

"I can pack the bat and cap," said Jack.

"Look at the sack!" said Dad.

3

Name _____

Short *a* Words

Find a list word to finish the sentence.
Write it on the line.

Spelling Words
at
can
cat
back
dad
am
bat
mad
ran
sack

1. The bug __**can**__ hop.

2. I __**am**__ sad.

3. His __**dad**__ has a van.

4. The dog __**ran**__ .

5. I __**bat**__ the ball.

6. Look __**at**__ the fox.

7. I fed my __**cat**__ .

8. Put the can in the __**sack**__ .

9. I know the __**way**__ to go.

10. I want to __**come**__ with you.

High-Frequency Words
way
come

© Pearson Education, Inc., 1

Home Activity Your child wrote spelling words to complete sentences. Help your child make up a new sentence for each spelling word.

Spelling Short a Words   **133**

Name _____

Sentences

Tell a story about when you did something with a pet.
Use some words from the box in your sentences.

> run   play   feed   watch

Possible answer: I run with my dog. We play a game. I throw a ball. He likes to run after it.

_____

- - - - - - - - - - - - - - - - - - -

_____

- - - - - - - - - - - - - - - - - - -

_____

School + Home

Home Activity Your child learned how to use sentences in writing. Have your child write two sentences that tell about a pet your family has had.

Name _____

Short *a* Words

Circle the word that names the picture.

Spelling Words

Spelling Words
at
can
cat
back
dad
am
bat
mad
ran
sack

1.
sack
can
(cat)

2.
cat
(bat)
dad

3.
back
(sack)
bat

4.
(dad)
ran
mad

5.
can
bat
(ran)

6.
(can)
ran
cat

Say the words. Circle the two words that are the same.
Write the word.

7. can (at) (at) am   7. **at**

8. (back) sack at (back)   8. **back**

9. ran (am) can (am)   9. **am**

10. ran (mad) (mad) dad   10. **mad**

School + Home

Home Activity Your child has been learning to spell words with short *a*. To review what your child has learned, take turns thinking of and spelling simple words with short *a*.

© Pearson Education, Inc., 1

Name _____

Sentences

Mark the group of words that is a sentence.

1. ⊗ Ron gets a pet today.
   ○ a pet today
   ○ gets a pet

2. ○ a big cat
   ⊗ The pet is a big cat.
   ○ the pet

3. ○ plays with his
   ○ with his cat
   ⊗ Ron plays with his cat.

4. ⊗ He rolls the ball to the cat.
   ○ ball to the cat
   ○ rolls the ball to

5. ○ hits the ball
   ○ the ball back
   ⊗ The cat hits the ball back.

6. ○ and the cat like
   ⊗ Ron and the cat like the game.
   ○ Ron and the cat

School + Home

Home Activity Your child prepared for taking tests on sentences. Read a story together. Have your child point out sentences in the story.

136 Conventions Sentences

Name _____

Say the word for each picture.
Write i on the line if you hear the **short i** sound.

p_i_g

---

1. _____
k __i__ ck

2. _____
h ____ ll

3. _____
t ____ ck

4. _____
f __i__ n

---

5. _____
p __i__ n

6. _____
d ____ g

7. _____
w __i__ g

8. _____
z __i__ p

Circle the word to finish each sentence. **Write** it on the line.

9. _____
I **will** go.

(will)   wall

10. _____
Sam **hid** the mat.

hip   (hid)

School + Home

Home Activity Your child practiced creating words with the short *i* sound heard in *pig*. Help your child make up fun rhymes using short *i* words, such as *The big pig in the wig can dig and do a jig.*

Name _____

Read the words in the box. **Pick** a word to finish each sentence.
Write it on the line. **Remember** to use a capital
letter at the beginning of a sentence.

| up   take   she   what |

1. My cat is ___**up**___ .

2. You can ___**take**___ two.

3. ___**She**___ has a pack.

4. ___**What**___ can Nan fix?

© Pearson Education, Inc., 1

School + Home **Home Activity** This week your child identified and read the words *up, take, she,* and *what.* As you read with your child, encourage him or her to point out these words in print.

Name _____

Read the story.
Circle the answer to each question about the story.

Jill and Meg play with a .

They hit the .

They pop the !

Jill and Meg are sad.

But Dad has a for them.

Jill and Meg play with the .

---

1. What happens first?
   Jill and Meg play with a .
   Jill and Meg are sad.

2. What happens that is sad?
   Jill and Meg kick the .
   Jill and Meg pop the .

3. What happens so Jill and Meg are not sad?
   Dad has a for Jill and Meg.
   Dad has a doll for Jill and Meg.

4. What happens last?
   Jill and Meg hit the .
   Jill and Meg play with the .

Home Activity Your child identified the plot, or what happens in a story, and the problem and solution in a story. Read a short fairy tale and have your child identify a problem and solution.

© Pearson Education, Inc., 1

Name _____

 Wise Owl

One day, Janey visited her friend, Wise Owl. He was sad.

"The animals come to ask me questions," he said. "Now I have a question. Whom should I ask?"

"I can help you," said Janey.

"I miss my brother and sister," Wise Owl said. "But my brother lives in the east. My sister lives in the west. I do not know where to go. What should I do?"

"Ask them to visit you!" said Janey.

Wise Owl smiled. "Thank you for your help," he said.

Key Features of a Fantasy Story

• Characters and events are made up.

• Characters do things that real people and animals cannot do.

Name _____

Say the word for each picture.
Write x on the line if the word has the same
ending sound as **ax**.

a<u>x</u>

---

1. **6**

si __X__

2.

wa __X__

3.

li _____

4.

ki _____

5.

bo __X__

6.

mi __X__

7.

si _____

8.

fi __X__

Write two words that have the same ending sound as **6**.

_____ _____

- - - - - - - - - - - - - - - - - - - - - - - - - - - - - - - - - -

_____ _____

© Pearson Education, Inc., 1

School + Home

Home Activity Your child practiced creating words that end with *x*. Write *six, mix,* and *fix* on cards. Have
your child choose a card, read the word, and use it in a sentence.

Name _____

Pig in a Wig

Short *i* Words

Write letters to finish the word.

<table><tr><td>Spelling Words</td></tr><tr><td>in</td></tr><tr><td>it</td></tr><tr><td>did</td></tr><tr><td>sit</td></tr><tr><td>six</td></tr><tr><td>fix</td></tr><tr><td>lip</td></tr><tr><td>mix</td></tr><tr><td>pin</td></tr><tr><td>wig</td></tr></table>

1. **pin**

2. **six**

3. **wig**

4. **lip**

5. **sit**

6. **mix**

7. **fix**

8. **in**

Write the missing words.

  it   did

9. I hit **it** .

10. Yes, I **did** .

 School + Home

Home Activity Your child spelled words with the short *i* vowel sound. Point to a picture on this page and have your child spell the word.

© Pearson Education, Inc., 1

Name _____

Subjects of Sentences

A sentence has a **naming part.** It names a person, place, animal, or thing. The naming part tells who or what the sentence is about.

Pat sees a pig.   **The pig** is big.

↑   ↑

naming part   naming part

Write the naming part of each sentence.

1. My pig is sick.

My pig

2. A vet can help the pig.

A vet

3. We go to the vet.

We

4. The pig feels better.

The pig

5. My dad thanks the vet.

My dad

Home Activity Your child learned about the naming parts of sentences. Read a story together. Point to several sentences. Ask your child to identify the naming part of each sentence.

Name _____

Story Chart

Title _____

Characters

Beginning

↓

Middle

↓

End of Story

Home Activity Your child planned a story. Share a brief story, and have your child tell what happens at the beginning.

Name _____

Trace and **write** the letters. Make sure you write your letters the correct size.

X   X   X

 x   x

Check children's work.

Copy the words. Leave the correct space between letters.

X-man   X-man

six   six

pig   pig

Ina   Ina

mix   mix

rip   rip

Did you leave the correct space between your letters? Yes   No

Home Activity Your child practiced writing words with *Ii* and *Xx*. Have your child practice writing each of these letters five more times.

Name _____

Read each question. **Circle** the correct answer.

1. What would you use to read a story about a frog?

2. What would you use to find the meaning of **vet**?

3. What would you use to find more about what vets do?

4. What would you use to find out what time the zoo opens?

5. What would you use to watch a show about animals?

 Home Activity Your child learned about sources that are available at a library or media center. Together with your child make a list of some of the sources found at a library. If possible, go to the library together and see how many of these sources you can find.

Jill Can!

Short i		Consonant x /ks/	High-Frequency Words
pick	zip	fit	six	is
quick	pin	sit	fix	the
Jill	rip	win		with
will	lid			

Jill is six.

Jill can zip.

Jill can pin the rip.

Jill can pick the bat.

Jill is quick!

Jill will win.

Decodable Story *Jill Can!*
Target Skill Short *i*, Consonant *x/ks/*

Jill can fix the lid.
The lid will fit.

Jill can pat the cat.
The cat will sit with Jill.

Name _____

Short *i* Words

Spelling Words				
in	it	did	sit	six
fix	lip	mix	pin	wig

High-Frequency Words
and
take

Circle a word to finish the sentence. **Write** the word.

1. He is   fix   (six)   pin .

2. I bit my   (lip)   did   sit .

3. Put   sit   (it)   fix   in the box.

4. Can she   in   wig   (fix) it?

5. You can   (sit)   lip   six   here.

6. His   did   (wig)   in   is red.

7. They   pin   six   (did)   not go.

8. Help me find a   (pin)   sit   in .

9. I will   did   pin   (take)   the book.

10. Jill   mix   (and)   six   Bob ran fast.

six

lip

it

fix

sit

wig

did

pin

take

and

School + Home

Home Activity Your child wrote spelling words to complete sentences. Read a sentence, say the spelling word, and ask your child to spell the word. Continue with other sentences.

Name _____

Subjects of Sentences

Complete each sentence with a naming part.
Possible answers:

1. **Blue** _____ is my favorite color.

2. **Cheese** _____ is my favorite food.

3. **Saturday** _____ is my favorite day.

Tell about things you like to do. **Write** your sentences.
Possible answer:

Baseball is my favorite sport.

I play video games. I like to

read funny books.

_____

_____

_____

Home Activity Your child learned how to use naming parts of sentences in writing. Ask your child to underline the naming parts of the sentences he or she wrote on the page.

© Pearson Education, Inc., 1

Name _____

Short *i* Words

Write the missing letters. Then write the words.

1. **it** ------------

2. **fix** ------------

3.   **in** ------------

4. **six** ------------

Spelling Words
in
it
did
sit
six
fix
lip
mix
pin
wig

Write a list word that rhymes with each word.

5. pig

wig ------------

6. hip

lip ------------

7. lid

did ------------

8. tin

pin ------------

9. fit

sit ------------

10. six

mix ------------

 School + Home

Home Activity Your child has been learning to spell words with short *i*. To review, draw some circles. Have your child write a short *i* word in each circle.

Name _____

Subjects of Sentences

Mark the sentence that has a line under the naming part.

1. ○ My mom <u>is</u> a vet.
   ⊗ <u>My mom</u> is a vet.
   ○ My mom is <u>a vet</u>.

2. ⊗ <u>She</u> helps sick animals.
   ○ She <u>helps</u> sick animals.
   ○ She helps <u>sick animals</u>.

3. ○ That dog cut <u>its</u> leg.
   ○ That dog <u>cut</u> its leg.
   ⊗ <u>That dog</u> cut its leg.

4. ⊗ <u>This cat</u> hurt its paw.
   ○ This cat hurt <u>its paw</u>.
   ○ This cat <u>hurt</u> its paw.

5. ○ A vet will fix <u>them</u>.
   ⊗ <u>A vet</u> will fix them.
   ○ A vet <u>will</u> fix them.

6. ○ The animals <u>like</u> my mom.
   ○ The animals like <u>my</u> mom.
   ⊗ <u>The animals</u> like my mom.

© Pearson Education, Inc., 1

School + Home

Home Activity Your child prepared for taking tests on the naming parts of sentences. Write simple sentences about your family, such as these: *Anne is your sister. Your mother works at a bank.* Ask your child to circle each naming part.

152 **Conventions** Subjects of Sentences

Name _____

Say the word for each picture.
Circle the picture if the word has
the **short o** sound you hear in **top.**

t**o**p

 1.

2.

3.

 4.

5.

6.

7.

8.

9.

10.

11.

12.

13.

14.

15.

© Pearson Education, Inc., 1

Home Activity Your child practiced creating words with the short o sound heard in _top_. Encourage your
child to use the short o words pictured above in sentences.

Name _____

Read the words in the box.
Pick a word to finish each sentence.
Write it on the line.

blue	from	help	little	get	use

1. Can I _____**use**_____ your ?

2. I can take it _____**from**_____ you.

3. I will _____**get**_____ a .

4. My dogs _____**help**_____ you go.

5. I see a big _____**blue**_____ ox!

6. The dogs are _____**little**_____ .

 School + Home

Home Activity This week your child identified and read the words *get, blue, from, help, little,* and *use.* Encourage your child to find these words in everyday print.

Name _____

Look at each pair of pictures.
Circle the pictures that show characters in settings that make sense. **Think** about what they are doing.

1.

2.

3.

Draw a picture of a character from a story doing something.
Show how he or she feels.

4. **Children's drawings should reveal information about the character's actions and feelings.**

School + Home **Home Activity** Your child learned about characters and places in a story. As you read together, have your child tell you what he or she knows about the characters and settings in the stories.

Name _____

 Kitty

Kitty's eyes are big and green.

She stretches, yawns, and licks her paws clean.

Key Features of a Short Poem

• A short poem has words written in lines that may rhyme.

• It can describe something or can express feelings.

Name _____

Circle a word to match each picture.

pan**s**

1.

bat   (bats)

2.

(mop)   mops

3.

rock   (rocks)

4.

pig   (pigs)

5.

top   (tops)

6.

cap   (caps)

7.

(kit)   kits

8.

sack   (sacks)

Write a sentence for each word.

_____
- -

9. cats _____

_____
- -

10. fox _____

Accept all reasonable responses.

Home Activity Your child identified singular and plural nouns. Have your child name items around the house. Point out the use of -s at the end of many plural words, such as *books, apples,* and *bowls.*

© Pearson Education, Inc., 1

Name _____

Short *o* Words

Spelling Words				
Mom	hot	hop	pot	pop
ox	lock	mop	got	rock

Write a word that rhymes.

1. **sock** on a

rock

2. **hot**

pot

3. **box** on an

ox

4. **block** on a

lock

5. **top** by a

mop

6. **Tom** and

Mom

Draw a line from the word to its shape.
Write the word in the shape.

hot

mop

pop

got

7. p o p

8. h o t

9. g o t

10. m o p

School + Home

Home Activity Your child spelled words with the short *o* vowel sound. Help your child spell each word and then think of a rhyming word.

Name _____

Predicates of Sentences

A sentence has an **action part**. It tells what a person or thing does.

The ox **helps**. He **pulls the wagon**.
↑ ↑
action part action part

Write the action part of each sentence.

1. The cow gives milk.

gives milk

2. Pop milks the cow.

milks the cow

3. The hen lays eggs.

lays eggs

4. Mom gets the eggs.

gets the eggs

5. The cat chases mice.

chases mice

Home Activity Your child learned about the action parts of sentences. Read a story together. Point to several sentences. Ask your child to identify the action part of each sentence.

Name _____

Web

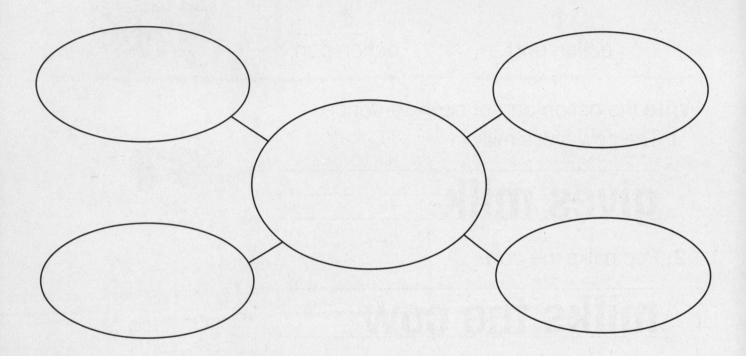

School + Home

Home Activity Your child is learning about writing a short poem. Talk with him or her about words that rhyme.

160 Writing Plan a Poem

Name _____

O   o

Copy the words. Write the letters from left to right.

Oz   Oz   job   job

pot   pot   hot   hot

box   box   not   not

mom   mom   got   got

cob   cob   sob   sob

doll   doll   rod   rod

log   log   fox   fox

Did you write the letters from left to right?   Yes   No

Home Activity Your child practiced writing words with O and o and the short o sound. Have your child choose two words from above and write the words three more times.

Name _____

How do animals help people?

1. **Use** the picture to think about a topic. **Write** two topic ideas.

Responses will vary. Possible responses: Animals help people.
We get food from animals. Life on a farm

2. **Circle** your favorite topic.
Responses will vary.

3. **Think** about what else you want to know about your topic.
Write three questions.

Questions will vary.

Home Activity Your child generated topic ideas for a picture and then formulated questions to research.
Discuss topics that your child is interested in and, if possible, look up information about one of the topics.

© Pearson Education, Inc., 1

What Is In the Box?

Short o		Plural -s + Consonant s/z/	High- Frequency Words	
box	not	rocks	are	go
fox	on	socks	in	is
got	top	mops	the	what
Dot				

Are rocks in the box?

Six rocks are in the box.

A fox is not in the box.

The fox is on top!

4

Decodable Story *What Is In the Box?*
Target Skills Skills Short *o*, Plural -*s* + Consonant *s/z/*

Are mops in the box?

The mops are in the box.

Dot got the socks.

The socks can go in the box.

Name _____

Short *o* Words

Find a list word to finish the sentence.
Write it on the line.

1. Fill the ____ **pot** ____ .

2. She is my ____ **mom** ____ .

3. I will ____ **mop** ____ up the mess.

4. Frogs can ____ **hop** ____ .

5. The sun is ____ **hot** ____ .

6. He is my ____ **pop** ____ .

7. Put a ____ **lock** ____ on his van.

8. I ____ **got** ____ wet.

9. I Will ____ **use** ____ my top?

10. Can you ____ **help** ____ me now.

Spelling Words
mom
hot
hop
pot
pop
ox
lock
mop
got
rock

High-Frequency Words
help
use

Home Activity Your child wrote spelling words to complete sentences. Have your child make up and write new sentences for several of the words.

Name _____

Predicates of Sentences

Complete each sentence. **Write** an action part. **Tell** what the animal does. **Possible answers:**

1. A horse **runs fast** .

2. A duck **swims** .

3. A dog **wags its tail** .

Tell about things that other animals do. **Use** words from the box or your own words. **Write** your sentences.

> swims   jumps   hops   runs

Possible answer:

A fish swims. A frog jumps.

A rabbit hops. A cat runs.

_____

© Pearson Education, Inc., 1

Home Activity Your child learned how to use action parts of sentences in writing. Ask your child to underline the action parts of the sentences he or she wrote on the page.

Name _____

Short *o* Words

Write the words in the puzzle.

Spelling Words

mom
hot
hop
pot
pop
ox
lock
mop
got
rock

Connect the matching hearts.

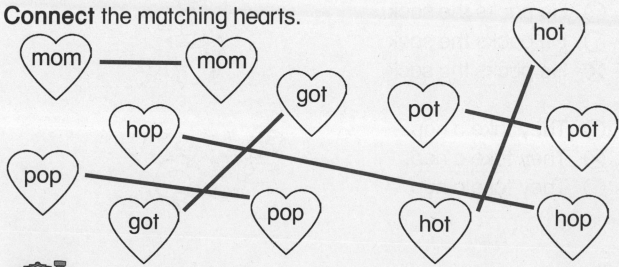

Home Activity Your child has been learning to spell words with short *o*. Have your child think of and write words that rhyme with *spot* or *stop*.

Name _____

Predicates of Sentences

Mark the sentence that has a line under the action part.

1. ○ Ox gets a mop.
   ⊗ Ox <u>gets a mop</u>.
   ○ Ox gets a <u>mop</u>.

2. ⊗ He <u>mops the pigs</u>.
   ○ He mops the pigs.
   ○ He mops the <u>pigs</u>.

3. ○ Mom and Pop ride on <u>Ox</u>.
   ○ Mom and <u>Pop</u> ride on Ox.
   ⊗ Mom and Pop <u>ride on Ox</u>.

4. ⊗ Ox <u>gets the cans</u>.
   ○ Ox gets the <u>cans</u>.
   ○ <u>Ox</u> gets the cans.

5. ○ He packs the <u>sack</u>.
   ○ He <u>packs</u> the sack.
   ⊗ He <u>packs the sack</u>.

6. ○ <u>They</u> take a nap.
   ⊗ They <u>take a nap</u>.
   ○ They take a <u>nap</u>.

Home Activity Your child prepared for taking tests on the action parts of sentences. Write simple sentences about your family, such as these: *Bill plays football. Your sister feeds the baby.* Ask your child to circle each action part.

© Pearson Education, Inc., 1

Name _____

Add -s to each word.
Write the new word on the line.

1. hop __**hops**__   2. sit __**sits**__

3. see __**sees**__ | 4. pat __**pats**__ | 5. help __**helps**__

Use the words you wrote to finish the sentences.
Write the words on the lines.

6. Jack __**sees**__ a big dog.

7. Jack __**pats**__ the dog.

8. Jack __**sits**__ on a rock.

9. The dog __**helps**__ Jack.

10. The dog __**hops**__ on Jack.

© Pearson Education, Inc., 1

School + Home   **Home Activity** Your child added -s to verbs. Have your child write the verbs *see, fan, nap, dig, sit, hop, jog,* and *mop,* and add an -s to each verb. Have your child pick a verb and use it in a sentence about you, such as *Mommy hops.* Then act out the sentence.

Name _____

Read the words in the box.
Pick a word to finish each sentence.
Write it on the line. **Remember** to begin a sentence with a capital letter.

eat	four	five	her	this	too

1. We see **four** .

2. The **eat** .

3. **This** is a big cat.

4. This is a big cat **too** .

5. Can we help **her** ?

6. We see **five** .

Home Activity This week your child identified and read the words *eat, four, five, her, too,* and *this.* Look through books to find these words in print and have your child read them aloud.

170   High-Frequency Words

© Pearson Education, Inc., 1

Name _____

Read each story.
Circle the sentence that tells best what the story is about.
Underline a detail that tells about the main idea.
Then **write** the topic of the story.

1. Dan has a cat.

   The cat is tan.

   The cat is fat.

   (Dan has a fat, tan cat.)

2. Topic:

   cat

   (cat)   mop

3. (Whales are big animals.)

   Whales have big tails.

   Whales have big fins.

   Whales eat a lot.

4. Topic:

   whales

   fins   (whales)

Write the name of a story you have read.
Draw a picture that shows what the story is about.

5. _____

Children should be able to name the story they illustrated. Have them tell you the main idea.

© Pearson Education, Inc., 1

Home Activity Your child learned about the main idea and details of a story. As you read stories together, have your child tell you the main idea.

Name _____

 The Loon

Last summer my family camped next to a lake. I liked waking up outside. Then I swam all day long!

One morning my dad took me to the lake. "Look!" he said. I saw a beautiful black bird floating on the lake.

"It is a loon," Dad said. "Loons can stay underwater a long time. They can dive deep and swim far. Watch!"

The loon dived underwater. We watched and waited. A minute later, we saw the loon again. I was amazed! It was so far away. We could hardly see it.

"If the loon comes again tomorrow, let's use our binoculars to watch," Dad said. I couldn't wait!

Key Features of a Personal Narrative

• The narrative tells a story about a real event in the author's life.

• It tells how the author feels about the event.

© Pearson Education, Inc., 1

Name _____

Add -ing to each word.
Write the new word on the line.

1. help **helping**   2. look **looking**

3. fix **fixing**   4. lick **licking**   5. play **playing**

Use the words you wrote to finish the sentences.
Write the words on the lines.

6. Jan is **looking** at the cats.

7. Jan is **helping** the cats.

8. The cats are **playing** with the can.

9. The big cat is **licking** the little cat.

10. Jan is **fixing** the lock.

© Pearson Education, Inc., 1

Home Activity Your child added -ing to verbs. Have your child write the verbs *lick, rock, kick, eat,* and *mix* on slips of paper. Then have your child add -ing to each verb. Have your child pick a slip of paper and act out the word for you to guess.

Phonics Inflected Ending -ing   **173**

Name _____

Inflected Ending -s

Write list words to finish the sentences.

© Pearson Education, Inc., 1

Spelling Words
nap
naps
sit
sits
win
wins
fit
fits
hit
hits

1. They **fit** .

2. It **fits** .

3. They **hit** .

4. He **hits** .

5. They **nap** in bed.

6. He **naps** in bed.

7. They **sit** on mats.

8. She **sits** on a mat.

9. They **win** the race.

10. He **wins** the race.

School + Home

Home Activity Your child spelled pairs of words with and without the -s ending. Point to a word on this page and have your child spell the other word in the pair.

Name _____

Declarative Sentences

A **telling sentence** tells something. It is a **declarative sentence**. It begins with a **capital letter**. It usually ends with a **period (.)**.

The fox has a kit.
The kit naps.

___

Find the sentence. **Underline** the sentence.

1. <u>The children see a fox.</u>

   the children see a fox

2. they see the kit

   <u>They see the kit.</u>

3. <u>The kit can run.</u>

   the kit can run

4. the fox and kit play

   <u>The fox and kit play.</u>

5. fox naps on the rocks

   <u>Fox naps on the rocks.</u>

Home Activity Your child learned about telling sentences. Read a story together. Have your child point to sentences in the story and name the capital letter at the beginning and the period at the end.

Name _____

Story Chart

Title _____

Beginning

Middle

End of Story

Home Activity Your child can plan to write about real events. Share a memory about an event such as a time you saw animals at a zoo.

Nn   Gg

Copy the words. Slant all of the letters the same way.

Gus   Gus   acting   acting

Nan   Nan   fixing   fixing

singing   singing   mixing   mixing

Gil   Gil   bumping   bumping

ringing   ringing   telling   telling

adding   adding   packing   packing

passing   passing   kicking   kicking

Do all of your letters slant the same way?   Yes   No

Home Activity Your child practiced writing words with *Nn* and *Gg* and words ending in *-ing*. Name a word from the chart, point to it, and have your child copy it on a separate sheet of paper. Continue with other words.

Name _____

Look at the chart. **Answer** the questions.

Adult Animals	Baby Animals
bear	cub
deer	fawn
elephant	calf
goat	kid

I. The topic of Lee's report is "Animals and Their Babies." Will this chart help?

_____

<u>**Yes, the chart gives information about what baby animals**</u>

_____

<u>**are called.**</u>

2. Is there enough information in the chart for Lee to write about "Animals and Their Babies"?

_____

<u>**No, the only information in the chart is the names of the**</u>

_____

<u>**animal babies. That is not enough.**</u>

3. Write a topic idea for Lee that uses only the information in the chart.

_____

_____

© Pearson Education, Inc., 1

Home Activity Your child learned how review and revise a topic. Ask your child to choose a topic that is of interest to him or her. Have him or her list some facts about the topic. Then using a reference source, read about the topic and ask your child to revise the facts based on your research.

Name _____

© Pearson Education, Inc., 1

Rob

Inflected ending -s		Inflected ending -ing	High-Frequency Words	
fills	sips	mixing	do	the
digs	mops	tossing	of	up
picks	naps	fixing	is	too
sits				

Rob will do lots of jobs.

Mom is mixing in the pot.

Rob fills the pan.

Kit sits and sips.

Rob mops up.

Kit naps. Rob naps, too!

4

Dad digs the rocks.

Rob is tossing the rocks in the box.

Tam is fixing the rip in the cap.

Rob picks up the pins.

Name _____

Inflected Ending -*s*

Write list words to finish the sentences.

© Pearson Education, Inc., 1

1. The pups __nap__ .

2. The pup __naps__ .

3. The pups __sit__ .

4. The pup __sits__ .

5. I can __win__ the game.

6. She __wins__ all the games.

7. The wind __hits__ the flag.

8. He can __hit__ the ball.

9. Will the hat fit her __too__ ?

10. My mitt fits __her__ .

Spelling Words
nap
naps
sit
sits
win
wins
fit
fits
hit
hits

High-Frequency Words
her
too

 School + Home

Home Activity Your child wrote spelling words to complete sentences. Have your child circle the list words that end in -*s*.

Name _____

Declarative Sentences

Which animals have you seen?

squirrel

fox

kit

deer

rabbit

Write about an animal you have seen.
Begin and **end** each sentence correctly.

Possible answer: I saw a squirrel last week. It was looking for nuts. I watched it a long time.

Home Activity Your child learned how to use telling sentences when writing. Take turns with your child saying sentences that describe the animals on the page.

Name _____

Inflected Ending -s

Draw a line to help Kit find her mitt.
Follow the words that rhyme with **Kit**.
Circle the words. **Write** the words.

Spelling Words
nap
naps
sit
sits
win
wins
fit
fits
hit
hits

1. **hit**   2. **fit**   3. **sit**

Write these words in ABC order.

(nap   wins   sits)

4. **nap**   5. **sits**   6. **wins**

Write these words in ABC order.

(win   hits   naps   fits)

7. **fits**   8. **hits**

9. **naps**   10. **win**

Home Activity Your child has been learning to spell words that end in -s. Help your child look on food boxes and cans for words that end in -s.

© Pearson Education, Inc., 1

Declarative Sentences

Find the sentence. **Mark** the sentence.

1. ○ the fox is red.
   ⊗ The fox is red.
   ○ the fox is red

2. ⊗ It has a kit.
   ○ it has a kit.
   ○ It has a kit

3. ○ the kit is brown.
   ○ the kit is brown
   ⊗ The kit is brown.

4. ⊗ The man has a pan.
   ○ the man has a pan.
   ○ The man has a pan

5. ○ the pan is tan
   ○ the pan is tan.
   ⊗ The pan is tan.

6. ○ the kit sits on the rocks.
   ⊗ The kit sits on the rocks.
   ○ the kit sits on the rocks

School + Home **Home Activity** Your child prepared for taking tests on telling sentences. Name a familiar animal. Have your child say a sentence that tells about the animal.

Name _____

Circle the word for each picture.

web

1.

mitt (men) man

2.

(bed) bid bad

3.

(pen) pan pin

4. **10**

tin tan (ten)

5.

jam (jet) jog

6.

(net) not nip

Circle the word the completes each sentence.

7. The fat _____ sits on my lap.

(hen) hat

8. I like my short _____ hat.

rid (red)

 School + Home **Home Activity** Your child practiced reading words with the short e sound heard in web. Work with your child to make words that rhyme with pet or bell.

© Pearson Education, Inc., 1

Name _____

Read the words in the box.
Pick a word to finish each sentence.
Write it on the line. **Remember** to use a capital letter at the beginning of a sentence.

> saw   small   tree   your

1. We _____ **saw** _____ a tree.

2. It was not a big _____ **tree** _____ .

3. Do you like this _____ **small** _____ tree?

4. _____ **Your** _____ tree is not wet.

© Pearson Education, Inc., 1

School + Home   **Home Activity** This week your child identified and read the words *saw*, *small*, *tree*, and *your*. Make flashcards with one word on each card. Mix them up and have your child read the words.

Name _____

Read each story.
Circle the sentence that tells best what the story is about.
Underline a detail that tells about the main idea.
Then **follow** the directions.

---

1. Ben has a hen.

   The hen is red.

   The hen is fat.

   (Ben has a fat, red hen.)

2. What is the topic of the story? **Write.**

   red   (hen)

---

3. Kim is a kid.

   Brad is a kid.

   Kim likes to play.

   Brad likes to play.

   (Kim and Brad like to play.)

4. **Write** your own main idea for the story.

   Possible response: Kim and Brad

---

5. (The bird has a nest in the tree.)

   The bird is big.

   The nest is small.

   The tree is tall.

6. **Write** your own main idea for the story.

   Possible response: The bird lives in a tree.

© Pearson Education, Inc., 1

School + Home

Home Activity Your child learned about the main idea and details of a story. As you read stories together, have your child tell you the main idea, or the most important point of the story.

Name _____

Little Squirrels

Luis and Lisa were playing at Lisa's house. They were running around and around.

"You are just like little squirrels!" Lisa's mom said. "The house is not for running! Go outside!"

Luis and Lisa went outside. "Why did your mom say that we are like squirrels?" Luis asked.

There was a big oak tree in the yard. Luis and Lisa sat under it. They watched the squirrels. The squirrels ran up the tree. The squirrels ran down the tree.

"Maybe we are like squirrels because we run so much!" Lisa said.

Key Features of a Realistic Story

• The characters, events, and setting seem real.

• Characters do things that really can happen.

Name _____

Pick letters from the box to finish each word.
Write the letters on the line.

 <u>sw</u>im

┌───┐
│ bl   cl   cr   dr   fl   fr   gr   sl   sm   st │
└───┘

1. _____ **fl** ag

2. _____ **bl** ock

3. _____ **cl** ap

4. _____ **dr** ess

5. _____ **cr** ab

6. _____ **fr** og

7. _____ **sm** ell

8. _____ **sl** ed

9. _____ **st** ep

10. _____ **gr** in

Home Activity Your child practiced creating words with initial blends *(flag, dress, sled)*. Help your child make up silly sentences that each contain words beginning with just one blend, such as *Freddy frog likes French fries.*

Name _____

Short e Words

Spelling Words				
bed	men	red	step	ten
net	leg	jet	sled	wet

Write three list words that rhyme with **pet**.

1. **net**   2. **jet**   3. **wet**

Write three list words that rhyme with **Ted**.

4. **bed**   5. **red**   6. **sled**

Write the missing word.

7. Let's make two **men** out of snow.

8. We need **ten** buttons.

9. Do not **step** on his hat.

10. Does he need a **leg** ?

leg
step
men
ten

© Pearson Education, Inc., 1

Home Activity Your child spelled words with the short e vowel sound. Have your child draw and label some of the words.

Name _____

Name _____

Interrogative Sentences

A **question** is an asking sentence. It is an **interrogative sentence**. It begins with a **capital letter**. It ends with a **question mark (?)**.

What will we see?
Is that a nest?

Put a ✓ by each question.

1. Who lives in the nest? ✓

   A bird lives in the nest. _____

2. The big bird is red. _____

   Is the big bird red? ✓

3. Can the big bird help? ✓

   The big bird can help. _____

4. I can get the eggs. _____

   Can you get the eggs? ✓

5. Where is the egg? ✓

   The egg is in the nest. _____

 Home Activity Your child learned about questions. Read a story together. Have your child find any questions in the story and name the capital letter at the beginning and the punctuation mark at the end.

Conventions Interrogative Sentences **191**

Name _____

Story Chart

Title _____

Characters

Setting

Beginning

↓

Middle

↓

End of Story

Home Activity Your child is learning about realistic stories. Have him or her describe a real place.

Name _____

E   e

Copy the words. Write the letters the correct size.

Emma	Emma	red	red
set	set	ten	ten
leg	leg	vest	vest
bed	bed	hen	hen
fell	fell	jet	jet
net	net	den	den
hem	hem	get	get

Did you write all of your letters the correct size?   ☐ Yes   ☐ No

Home Activity Your child practiced writing words with *E* and *e* and the short *e* sound. Have your child write as many words with *E* or *e* that he or she can think of that are not on this page. You can use the words from above to help your child write rhyming words.

Name _____

Look at the lists.
Follow the directions and **answer** the questions.

Wild Animals	Pets
bear	cat
fox	dog
frog	fish
lion	frog
tiger	hamster

I. **Think** of two more wild animals. **Write** the animal names.

_____ _____

__Accept any wild animals__ _____

2. **Think** of two more pets. **Write** the animal names.

_____ _____

__Accept any pets__ _____

3. **Circle** the animal that you would like to know more about.
Responses will vary.

4. **Think** about what else you want to know about your animal.
Write two questions.

__Questions will vary. Possible responses: Where do tigers live?__
__What do tigers eat?__ _____

_____

Home Activity Your child learned how to identify topics and ask questions about a topic. Ask your child to make up another question about one of the topics above.

© Pearson Education, Inc., 1

The Blocks

Short *e*	Initial consonant blends	High Frequency Words
Meg	blocks	the
gets	black	a
ten	step	up
red	stack	help
sets		
bed		
fell		
Peg		
mess		
yells		

Meg gets ten blocks.

Meg has red blocks.

Meg has black blocks.

"Pick up the blocks," Mom yells.

"Peg will help!"

4

Meg sets the blocks on the step.

Meg will stack the blocks on the bed.

2

The blocks fell.

Peg got Mom.

"Meg has a mess!"

3

Name _____

Short e Words

Spelling Words

| bed | men | red | step | ten | net | leg | jet | sled | wet |

Choose a word to finish the sentence.
Fill in the circle. **Write** the word.

1. I made the ● bed ○ men ○ leg .

bed

2. Do not get me ○ step ● wet ○ net !

wet

3. Her sock was ○ sled ○ jet ● red .

red

4. Kick with your ○ ten ○ net ● leg .

leg

5. Kim has a ○ red ● sled ○ wet .

sled

6. A fish is in the ● net ○ ten ○ step .

net

7. Sit on the ○ ten ● step ○ red .

step

8. I will count to ● ten ○ jet ○ sled .

ten

Write the words and complete the sentence.

9. I ____ **saw** ____ **your** ____ sled.

High-Frequency Words

saw

your

Home Activity Your child wrote spelling words to complete sentences. Help your child find other spelling words that make sense in the sentences. For example, sentence 1 could read "I made the **net**."

Name _____

Interrogative Sentences

Finish the question. **Write** an animal name.

a bird

a cat

a dog

an elephant

an ostrich

What does **Answers will vary.** look like?

Read the sentence. **Change** the words to make a question.
Write the question.

The bird is red.

Is the bird red?

_____

_____

_____

_____

Home Activity Your child learned how to use questions when writing. Say a sentence about one of the animals on the page, such as *The elephant is big*. Have your child write your sentence as a question: *Is the elephant big?*

Name _____

Short *e* Words

Write the words.

1. **net**
2. **jet**

3. **leg**
4. **step**

Circle the word that matches. **Write** it.

5. bed   (bed)   red
6. men   wet   (men)
7. ten   net   (ten)
8. sled   step   (sled)
9. red   (red)   sled
10. wet   net   (wet)

Spelling Words
bed
men
red
step
ten
net
leg
jet
sled
wet

bed

men

ten

sled

red

wet

 School + Home

Home Activity Your child has been learning to spell words with short *e*. Have your child think of and write words that rhyme with *set* or *fed*.

Name _____

Interrogative Sentences

Find the question. **Mark** the question.

1. ○ The nest big is.
   ○ is the nest big?
   ⊗ Is the nest big?

2. ⊗ Do birds live here?
   ○ Birds do live here.
   ○ do birds live here?

3. ○ can you see the nest?
   ○ You can see the nest.
   ⊗ Can you see the nest?

4. ○ The big twig hit the nest.
   ⊗ Will the big twig hit the nest?
   ○ will the big twig hit the nest?

5. ○ are the birds in the nest?
   ⊗ Are the birds in the nest?
   ○ The birds in the nest are.

6. ⊗ Do you see eggs in the nest?
   ○ do you see eggs in the nest?
   ○ You do see eggs in the nest.

Home Activity Your child prepared for taking tests on questions. Together listen to a conversation or an interview on TV. Each time your child hears a question, have him or her say "Question!"

Name _____

Say the word for each picture.
Write u on the line if you hear the **short u** sound.

p<u>u</u>p

1. b_<u>u</u>_g

2. d_<u>u</u>_ck

3. b_<u>u</u>_s

4. h_<u>u</u>_g

5. b_____x

6. dr_<u>u</u>_m

7. s_<u>u</u>_n

8. sl_____d

Write a sentence for each word.

9. mud _____

10. plum _____

Make sure children used <u>mud</u> and <u>plum</u> in their sentences.

Home Activity Your child identified and created words with the short *u* sound heard in *pup*. Work with your child to write words that rhyme with *rug*.

Name _____

Read the words in the box.
Pick a word to finish each sentence.
Write it on the line.

home   into   many   them

1. This is a ___**home**___ for .

2. We see ___**many**___ .

3. Do you see ___**them**___ ?

4. The go ___**into**___ the home.

Draw a picture of you going into your home.

5.

**Picture should show
child going into his or her home.**

 Home Activity Your child identified and read the words *home, into, many,* and *them.* Invite your child to use the words to describe life in his or her home.

Name _____

Look at the picture that shows what happened.
Circle the picture that shows why it happened.

Read the two story sentences. **Circle** the one that tells what happens.

4. The bell rang.   The pup ran.

5. Sam is sick.   Sam naps in bed.

Home Activity Your child learned about cause (why something happens) and effect (what happens). Look for cause and effect with your child. For example, you might point out that when the temperature drops in the fall, frost forms.

Comprehension Cause and Effect   203

Name _____

Writing Prompt: Write a composition about an animal you like.

 Rabbits

I like rabbits. My mom and I watch rabbits in our yard. We see them in the evening. They eat and play at night. They rest during the day.

Rabbits eat plants. We try to keep them away from our garden.

Rabbits stand very still. They do not want us to see them! If I go too near to a rabbit, it hops away.

I learn a lot by watching rabbits.

Name _____

Say the word for each picture.
Circle the letters that finish each word.
Write the letters on the line.

 ne<u>st</u>

(nd)   nt

1. po **nd**

nt   (mp)

2. ju **mp**

mp   (nt)

3. de **nt**

(st)   nt

4. ca **st**

st   (mp)

5. la **mp**

nt   (nd)

6. ha **nd**

(st)   nt

7. ve **st**

(nt)   mp

8. te **nt**

nt   (st)

9. fi **st**

(mp)   st

10. sta **mp**

School + Home

Home Activity Your child created words using final consonant blends such as *mp, nd, nt,* and *st*. Have your child make up sentences using words from this page.

Name _____

Short *u* Words with Final Consonant Blends

Spelling Words				
just	dust	must	hunt	crust
bump	jump	trust	trunk	dusk

Write a list word to name the picture.

1. **crust** 2. **jump** 3. **trunk**

Read the clue. **Write** the list word.

4. It starts with **j**. It rhymes with **must**.

5. It starts with **d**. It rhymes with **husk**.

6. It starts with **h**. It rhymes with **stunt**.

7. It starts with **m**. It rhymes with **just**.

8. It starts with **tr**. It rhymes with **dunk**.

9. It starts with **tr**. It rhymes with **dust**.

10. It starts with **b**. It rhymes with **pump**.

just

dusk

hunt

must

trunk

trust

bump

School + Home **Home Activity** Your child wrote words with the short *u* vowel sound. Take turns with your child making up clues and then guessing and spelling the word.

Name _____

Exclamatory Sentences

An **exclamatory sentence** is a sentence that shows strong feeling. It begins with a **capital letter**. It ends with an **exclamation mark (!).**

The animal is big!

Underline each sentence that is an exclamation.

1. That hippo is funny!

2. It looks mad!

3. Where does it live?

4. It can live in the mud.

5. Now the hippo is happy!

6. I like the hippo.

Home Activity Your child learned about exclamations. Have your child read each exclamation on this page with strong feeling. Then take turns with your child saying exclamations of your own.

Name _____

Composition
Top-Score Response

Focus/Ideas	A good composition tells about one topic.
Organization	A good composition tells important ideas in an order that makes sense.
Voice	A good composition tells about the topic in a way that is interesting.
Word Choice	A good composition uses clear words.
Sentences	A good composition is written in complete sentences.
Conventions	A good composition has sentences that are punctuated correctly.

Home Activity Your child can begin to learn about writing on writing tests. Ask how writing a composition about a topic such as real animals is different from making up a story.

Name _____

Q q   U u

Copy the words. Leave the correct space between each letter.

Quin   Quin

Uta   Uta

quick   quick

bus   bus

quit   quit

fun   fun

quack   quack

tub   tub

sun   sun

quiz   quiz

duck   duck

hug   hug

mug   mug

jug   jug

Did you leave the correct space between each letter?   Yes   No

Home Activity Your child practiced writing words with *Qq* and *Uu* and words with short *u* sound. Have your child copy this sentence as neatly as possible: *Quin and Uta quickly run to the bus.*

© Pearson Education, Inc., 1

Name _____

Use the picture to choose and revise a topic.

1. **Name** three animals you see. **Circle** the animal you would like to know more about. **Responses will vary.**

2. What more would you like to know about this animal? **Write** two questions.

_____

Responses will vary.

_____

_____

3. Use your questions. **Write** your new topic. Ask for help if needed.

_____

Responses will vary. Responses should narrow the topic to one or two things about the animal.

© Pearson Education, Inc., 1

 Home Activity Your child learned how to answer questions about a topic. Encourage your child to ask questions about the topic "Preparing a Family Meal." After the questions are answered, ask your child if he or she wants to reword the topic.

The Test

Short u		Final Consonant Blends		High-Frequency Words	
Huff	fun	test	must	the	said
Bud	stuck	best		a	is
sum	sums				

"The class will get a test," said Miss Huff.

"The class will add."

1

Bud got the sums.

Bud did his best.

Bud did well!

4

Decodable Story The Test
Target Skills Short *u*, Final Consonant Blends

1.3.A.1.ii.5 Decode words in context by applying common letter-sound correspondences, including: single letters (vowels) including short *u*. **Also 1.3.A.1.iii, 1.3.H.2.**

1 + 1. Bud gets the sum.

3 + 3. The sum is six.

The test is fun!

5 + 5. Bud is stuck.

Bud must get the sum.

The sum is ten.

Name _____

Short *u* Words with Final Consonant Blends

Spelling Words				
just	dust	must	hunt	crust
bump	jump	trust	trunk	dusk

Write a list word to name the picture.

1. It is __dusk__ .

2. I see the __dust__ .

3. I __trust__ you.

4. I __just__ want to run.

5. I __hunt__ for an egg.

6. Mom eats a __crust__ .

7. I __jump__ into the car.

8. The car has a __trunk__ .

9. The car hits a __bump__ .

10. We __must__ go on the bus.

Home Activity Your child wrote spelling words to complete a story. Help your child use some of the words in a story about his or her day.

© Pearson Education, Inc., 1

Name _____

Exclamatory Sentences

What animal would you like to have?
Write about the animal.
Use an exclamation to show how you felt.

a zebra   an elephant   a lion   an ostrich   a hippo

_____
- -
_____
- -
_____
- -
_____
- -
_____

Read the question. **Change** the words to make an exclamation.
Write the exclamation.

Is the pet big?

_____

The pet is big!

© Pearson Education, Inc., 1

School + Home

Home Activity Your child learned how to use exclamations in writing. Name an object in the room and a word that describes the object *(lamp/bright; sofa/big; pillow/soft; rug/dark).* Have your child write exclamations using the word pairs *(The lamp is too bright! That pillow is so soft!).*

Name _____

Short *u* Words with Final Consonant Blends

Write the words in the puzzle.

© Pearson Education, Inc., 1

Spelling Words

just

bump

dust

jump

must

trust

hunt

trunk

crust

dusk

Write the missing words.

trust   dusk   must   just

5. I always **trust** you.

6. I **must** get the ball.

7. I **just** want to play.

8. It is **dusk** now.

Home Activity Your child has been learning to spell words with short *u*. Help your child find words with short *u* in library books or schoolbooks.

Spelling Short *u* Words with Final Consonant Blends   **215**

Name _____

Exclamatory Sentences

Mark the correct exclamation.

1. ○ the big bird cannot fly!
   ⊗ The big bird cannot fly!
   ○ The big bird cannot fly

2. ⊗ The bird is so big!
   ○ The bird is so big
   ○ the bird is so big!

3. ○ the zebra loves the park!
   ○ The zebra loves the park
   ⊗ The zebra loves the park!

4. ⊗ Look at the big hippo!
   ○ Look at the big hippo
   ○ Look at the big hippo?

5. ○ The zebra is fast
   ⊗ The zebra is fast!
   ○ the zebra is fast

6. ○ Oh no, the bird fell
   ○ oh no, the bird fell!
   ⊗ Oh no, the bird fell!

Home Activity Your child prepared for taking tests on exclamations. Together read a favorite book. Have your child point out the exclamations and tell how he or she knew they were exclamations.

Name _____

Say the word for each picture.
Write sh or **th** to finish each word.

di**sh**   **th**ink

1.
_____
sh op

2.
fi _____
sh

3.
_____
th in

4.
_____
sh ell

5.
ba _____
th

6.
bru _____
sh

Circle a word to finish each sentence. **Write** the word.

 path   math
_____

7. She walked on the bike **path** .

---

drip   ship
_____

8. I saw the **ship** from the beach.

School + Home

Home Activity Your child added the digraphs *th* and *sh* (two letters that together stand for one sound) to complete words. Have your child copy the words that contain *sh* from this page and use as many of those words as possible in one sentence. Repeat using the *th* words.

Name _____

Read the words in the box.
Pick a word from the box to finish each sentence.
Write it on the line.

catch	good	no	put	said	want

1. Dad and Bob __**want**__ to fish.

2. "You can __**put**__ it here," Dad said.

3. "I will," __**said**__ Bob.

4. Bob has __**no**__ fish yet.

5. Bob can __**catch**__ that fish!

6. It is a __**good**__ fish.

Home Activity Your child identified and read the words *catch, good, no, put, said,* and *want.* As you read with your child, encourage him or her to point out these words in print.

Name _____

Read the story.
Follow the directions.

Ted sees a nest fall from a tree.

It has three blue eggs in it.

Ted picks up the nest.

Ted sets the nest back in the tree.

I. **Write** a sentence that tells what happens at the beginning of the story.

Ted sees a nest fall from a tree.

2. **Write** a sentence that tells what happens in the middle of the story.

Ted picks up the nest.

3. **Draw** a picture that shows what happens at the end of the story. Then **act out** what happened in the story.

> **Check children's drawings.**
> **Drawings should show a nest**
> **in the branches of a tree.**

Home Activity Your child learned about the order in which things happen in a story. Reread this story with your child. Ask your child to tell you what might happen next in the story.

Name _____

Dear Uncle Karl,

My favorite thing is fishing. I want you to go with me. We can go to the pond down the road. Then we will catch a bunch of fish. It will be really exciting! I hope you can go with me.

Your niece,
Lynn

Key Features of a Friendly Letter

• It begins with a greeting and ends with a closing.

• It often tells how the writer feels.

• It can tell ideas in time order, or sequence.

Name _____

Circle a word to finish each sentence.
Write it on the line.

 b**a**ll

---

 mall   mill

1. We met Dad at the _____ **mall** .

---

well   walk

2. We take a _____ **walk** and talk.

---

tell   tall

3. Dad got a _____ **tall** bag.

---

all   ill

4. We _____ **all** go in.

---

smell   small

5. I am too _____ **small** to see!

Home Activity Your child practiced reading words with the vowel sound heard in *ball* and *walk*. Work with your child to write a list of words that rhyme with *ball*.

Name _____

Words with *sh, th*

Spelling Words				
ship	fish	then	shut	with
rush	shell	shop	trash	thin

Find a list word to name the picture. **Write** it.

1. **ship**

2. **shop**

3. **trash**

4. **fish**

5. **shell**

6. **shut**

Unscramble the word. **Write** the word.

s	h	u	r

7. **rush**

i	t	h	w

8. **with**

n	e	t	h

9. **then**

n	t	h	i

10. **thin**

School + Home

Home Activity Your child wrote words with the *sh* or *th* sound. Say a list word. Ask if it has *sh* or *th*. Have your child spell the word.

© Pearson Education, Inc., 1

Name _____

Common Nouns

A **noun** names a person, a place, an animal, or a thing.

The word **man** names a person.

The word **park** names a place.

The word **fish** names an animal.

The word **net** names a thing.

Write the noun for each picture. **Say** a sentence for each noun.

Person

girl   boy

1. **girl**

Place

city   pond

2. **pond**

Animal

cat   rabbit

3. **rabbit**

Thing

box   pan

4. **box**

Home Activity Your child learned about nouns. Read a story together. Have your child point to nouns in the story and tell whether they name people, places, animals, or things.

Name _____

Letter Format

Dear _____ ,

_____

_____

_____

_____

_____

_____

_____

                    _____

                    _____ ,

Home Activity Your child is learning about writing letters. Help him or her plan a letter to a relative or family friend.

224 **Writing** Plan

S s   H h

Copy the words. Write the letters the correct size.

Shem   Shem   shack   shack

Hal   Hal   dish   dish

shop   shop   rash   rash

fish   fish   mush   mush

wish   wish   cash   cash

shut   shut   Hank   Hank

ship   ship   rush   rush

Did you write all of your letters the correct size?

© Pearson Education, Inc., 1

Home Activity Your child practiced writing words with *Ss* and *Hh* and short vowels. Have your child choose two words from the chart and write the words three more times.

Name _____

Ned's New Dog
Contents

1. Draw a circle around the page numbers.

2. Put a box around the chapter titles.

3. Write the name of the last chapter.

Good Dog, Spot!

4. Write the page number on which "Ned's New Plan" begins.

39

5. Write the total number of chapters in "Ned's New Dog."

10

Home Activity Your child learned to use the table of contents in a storybook to find information. As you read together, point out the table of contents and encourage your child to help you find information such as the page number for a specific chapter.

© Pearson Education, Inc., 1

Cans

Consonant Digraphs	Vowel Sound in *ball* and *walk*	High-Frequency Words
shed	all	she
trash	walk	the
crush	talks	to
smash		do
cash		
Smith		
with		
then		

Miss Smith has cans.

She will not fill the trash with cans.

Miss Smith talks with Ned.

"Do not fill the land with trash!"

Decodable Story Cans
Target Skills Consonant Digraphs, Vowel Sound in *ball* and *walk*

Miss Smith will walk to the shed.

She will crush and smash the cans.

Miss Smith will fill all the bins with cans.

Then she will get cash.

Name _____

Words with *sh, th*

Find a list word or high-frequency word to finish the sentence.
Write it on the line.

Spelling Words

ship
fish
then
shut
with
rush
shell
shop
trash
thin

1. I will __**rush**__ home.

2. Will you feed my __**fish**__ ?

3. Come __**with**__ me.

4. Dad did a __**good**__ job.

5. Put the paper in the __**trash**__ can.

6. This egg has a brown __**shell**__ .

7. Do not __**shut**__ the door.

8. I __**want**__ to buy a new cap.

9. She came on a __**ship**__ .

10. That dog is __**thin**__ .

High-Frequency Words

want
good

Home Activity Your child wrote spelling words and high-frequency words to complete sentences. Ask your child to write a sentence using two or more of the words.

© Pearson Education, Inc., 1

Name _____

Common Nouns

Write about things you do with your family.
Use words from the box or words of your own.

```
mom    dad    brother
grandma   grandpa   sister
```

Possible answer: I watch football with my dad. I play the piano with my mom. My brother and I like to play games.

Choose other nouns. **Say** a sentence for each noun.

Home Activity Your child learned how to use nouns in writing. Write sentences about family members, such as *Your sister has brown hair. Your mother loves flowers.* Have your child circle the nouns in the sentences.

Name _____

Words with *sh, th*

Read the clue. **Write** a list word.

It rhymes with

1. **shell**

It rhymes with

2. **then**

It rhymes with

3. **thin**

It rhymes with

4. **ship**

Find a list word in each row of letters.
Circle it. **Write** it.

r u s h t e   5. **rush**

t s h u t r   6. **shut**

s h o p t h   7. **shop**

s t r a s h   8. **trash**

w i f i s h   9. **fish**

r w i t h s   10. **with**

Spelling Words
ship
fish
then
shut
with
rush
shell
shop
trash
thin

fish
shut
trash
rush
shop
with

Home Activity Your child has been learning to spell words with *sh* and *th*. Have your child circle *sh* and *th* in the spelling words.

Name _____

Common Nouns

Mark the noun that completes the sentence.

1. Max wants a ____.
   - ○ eat
   - ⊗ fish
   - ○ will

2. The ____ has a pond.
   - ○ in
   - ○ sit
   - ⊗ park

3. Max got a red ____.
   - ⊗ ball
   - ○ talk
   - ○ this

4. A ____ is in the net.
   - ○ call
   - ○ and
   - ⊗ shell

5. The ____ gave them a fish.
   - ○ fat
   - ⊗ woman
   - ○ that

Home Activity Your child prepared for taking tests on nouns. Together read a simple piece of mail, such as an ad. Have your child circle the nouns in the article.

Name _____

Circle the word for each picture.

 cake

1.

(rake)   rack

2.

snack   (snake)

3.

frog   (frame)

4.

(can)   cane

5.

(cape)   cap

6.

(plane)   plan

Choose a word to finish each sentence. **Write** the word on the line.

(lake)   lock

7. I like to swim in the _____**lake**_____.

plant   (plate)

8. Please put the food on the _____**plate**_____.

gum   (game)

9. Will you play this _____**game**_____ with me?

gate   (skate)

10. I can _____**skate**_____ fast.

School + Home

Home Activity Your child practiced reading words with the long *a* sound spelled *a _ e*, such as *cake*. Work with your child to write a list of words that rhyme with *cake*. Repeat with *cave*.

© Pearson Education, Inc., 1

Name _____

Read the words in the box.
Pick a word to finish each sentence.
Write it on the line.

| be   could   horse   of   old   paper |

1. Dad gave me a __**horse**__ .

2. She was not __**old**__ .

3. She __**could**__ run and jump.

4. I put her name on a __**paper**__ .

5. I can make the horse the color __**of**__ a fox.

6. We will __**be**__ pals!

 Home Activity Your child identified and read the words *be, of, could, horse, old,* and *paper*. Write these words on small pieces of paper or self-stick notes. Tape them on a mirror or desk for your child to practice every day.

© Pearson Education, Inc., 1

234 **High-Frequency Words**

Name _____

Look at the first picture that shows what happened.
Circle the picture that shows why it happened.

1.

2.

3.

4.

Look at the picture that shows what happened.
Draw a picture that shows why it happened.

5.   **Picture should show
boy raking leaves.**

© Pearson Education, Inc., 1

Home Activity Your child learned about cause (why something happens) and effect (what happens). Call your child's attention to causes and effects by asking questions such as: *What happened?* (effect) *Why did it happen?* (cause)

Comprehension Cause and Effect **235**

Name _____

 Group Time

Every day we have group time. I work with José and Kim. We help each other with math. Sometimes we change papers. We talk about stories. We answer questions. Then we share with the class.

Key Features of a Brief Composition

· It tells interesting facts.

· It tells about one topic.

Name _____

Circle the word for each picture.
Write it on the line.

 lace

 age

1.

(face) fake

face

2.

rake (race)

race

3.

cave (cage)

cage

4.

(wag) wage

wag

5.

speck (space)

space

6.

(stage) stake

stage

7.

(track) trace

track

8.

pace (page)

page

Circle the word to finish each sentence. **Write** the word.

(lace)   brake

9. I tripped on my ___ **lace** ___ .

page   (cage)

10. My pet bird lives in a ___ **cage** ___ .

 Home Activity Your child practiced reading and writing words that have the sound that *c* stands for in *lace* and the sound that *g* stands for in *age*. Ask your child to write a list of words that rhyme with *lace* and a list of words that rhyme with *age*.

Name _____

Words with Long *a*

Spelling Words				
face	made	age	safe	take
make	cage	cake	late	name

Write three list words that rhyme with **rake**.

1. **take**   2. **make**   3. **cake**

Write two list words that rhyme with **page**.

4. **age**   5. **cage**

Write the missing word.

safe   face   name   late   made

6. Her **name** is Bo.

7. Bo **made** a dog.

8. Her **face** is happy.

9. Is that ball **safe** ?

10. Can we stay **late** ?

Home Activity Your child wrote words with the long *a* sound. Help your child think of words that rhyme with the spelling words.

© Pearson Education, Inc., 1

Name _____

Proper Nouns

Special names for people, places, animals, and things are called **proper nouns.** Proper nouns begin with capital letters.

Meg

Rose Pond

Rex

Tell Tower

Look at each picture. **Write** the proper name on the line.
Say a sentence for each proper noun.

Beth

1. This girl is **Beth** .

Hall School

2. Beth goes to **Hall School** .

Post Road

3. The school is on **Post Road** .

Coco

4. The class pet is **Coco** .

School + Home

Home Activity Your child learned about proper nouns. Read a story together. Have your child point to proper nouns in the story.

Name _____

Idea Web

Decorating the Classroom

We decorate the classroom for special days like Thanksgiving.

We put our pictures on the walls and doors.

We draw pictures for decorations.

Home Activity Your child has thought of ideas for writing about how children work together. Share ideas about how people do things together at home.

Name _____

P   p

Copy the words. Leave the correct space between the letters.

Page   Page   wage   wage

pace   pace   lace   lace

pave   pave   race   race

tape   tape   shade   shade

cape   cape   pale   pale

cage   cage   pane   pane

face   face   rage   rage

Did you leave the correct space between your letters?   Yes   No

Home Activity Your child practiced writing words with *P* and *p*. Have your child find two pairs of rhyming words in the list above and write the words two more times as neatly as possible.

© Pearson Education, Inc., 1

Name _____

custodian – a person who helps keep buildings clean and safe

librarian – a person trained to work in a library

teacher – a person who helps people learn

1. Circle the school helper you would like to know more about.
Responses will vary.

2. What would you like to know? Write three interview questions.

Responses will vary.

_____

_____

_____

3. Ask your interview questions. Write one thing you learned.

Responses will vary.

Home Activity Your child learned how to interview. Have your child make a list of family members or friends that he or she would like to interview. Help your child come up with some interesting questions for the interview.

Name _____

The Race

Long *a*: *a_e*			Consonants *c* /s/ and *g* /j/	High-Frequency Words	
Jake	gate	lane	race	I	see
lake	late	shape	pace	the	is
cake	skates	shade	place	of	for
takes	waves		age		
ate	came		Page		

Jake waves at Page. "I am in shape!"

"I will win the race at the lake."

Jake takes the right lane.

See Jake dash past the gate.

Jake is fast for his age!

Decodable Story *The Race*
Target Skills Long *a: a_e*, Consonants *c* /s/, *g* /j/

Page waves at Jake.

"I came late. I ate lots of cake.

I will get last place."

Page walks in the shade.

She is not fast.

"I wish I had skates!"

Name _____

Words with Long *a*

Spelling Words				
face	made	age	safe	take
make	cage	cake	late	name

High-Frequency Words
could
old

Circle a word to finish the sentence. **Write** the word.

1. I love (cake) late make!

__cake__

2. Have a face (safe) name trip.

__safe__

3. I (made) age cake it.

__made__

4. What is your made late (name)?

__name__

5. His age (face) make got red.

__face__

6. What is in the (cage) age face?

__cage__

7. She won't tell her cake late (age).

__age__

8. Let's safe made (make) a kite.

__make__

9. I (could) cage cake stay up late.

__could__

10. That is an age (old) take cage.

__old__

Home Activity Your child used spelling words to complete sentences. Have your child identify and write as many spelling words as possible to finish this sentence: *This is my_____ .*

Name _____

Proper Nouns

Finish each sentence with a proper noun. **Answers will vary.**

My teacher is _____.
(name of your teacher)

My school is _____.
(name of your school)

Write the names of three children in your class.

_____ _____ _____

Tell something about each child.

Possible answer: Tim tells jokes.

Anna can dance.

Carmen can read.

Home Activity Your child learned how to use proper nouns in writing. Write sentences about people that you and your child know, such as *Steve is a friend. Maria is our cousin.* Have your child circle the proper nouns in the sentences.

© Pearson Education, Inc., 1

Name _____

Words with Long *a*

Spelling Words

face	made	age	safe	take
make	cage	cake	late	name

Use this code. **Write** the words.

1. age

2. face

3. make

4. cake

5. made

6. cage

7. safe

8. name

9. take

Write the missing letters. **Write** the word.

10. l a t e   late

Home Activity Your child has been learning to spell words with long *a*. Ask your child to explain how all the list words are alike. (All have long *a*, and all end in *a*-consonant-*e*.)

Name _____

Proper Nouns

Mark the sentence that uses the proper noun correctly.

1. ○ This boy is jake.
   ⊗ This boy is Jake.
   ○ This boy is JAKE.

2. ○ He has a dog named PIP.
   ○ He has a dog named pip.
   ⊗ He has a dog named Pip.

3. ⊗ This girl is Grace.
   ○ This girl is GRACE.
   ○ This girl is grace.

4. ○ She has a cat named KIT.
   ○ She has a cat named kit.
   ⊗ She has a cat named Kit.

5. ⊗ The children go to Tam School.
   ○ The children go to tam School.
   ○ The children go to Tam school.

6. ○ The school is on elm Street.
   ⊗ The school is on Elm Street.
   ○ The school is on Elm street.

School + Home

Home Activity Your child prepared for taking tests on proper nouns. Together read a short newspaper or magazine article. Have your child circle the proper nouns in the article.

Name _____

Circle the word for each picture.

9 nine

1.

   (vine)   vane

2.

   mane   (mice)

3.

   (wig)   wipe

4.

   (bike)   bill

Say the name of each picture.
Write the letters to finish each word.

5.

   p i l e

6.

   sl i de

7.

   sh i ne

8.

   k i te

Pick a word to finish each sentence. **Write** the word on the line.

(slice)   price

9. I bought a __**slice**__ of pizza.

(bite)   rice

10. "Would you like a __**bite**__?" I asked.

School + Home   **Home Activity** Your child practiced reading words with the long *i* sound spelled *i _ e*, such as *nine*. Work with your child to write a list of words that rhyme with *nine*. Repeat with *hide*.

© Pearson Education, Inc., 1

Name _____

Read the words in the box.
Pick a word to finish each sentence.
Write it on the line. **Remember** to use capital letters at the beginning of a sentence.

live   out   people   who   work

1. **Who** can fix this clock?

2. The **people** in the shop can fix it.

3. They will **work** on it.

4. Where does your dog **live** ?

5. His home is **out** here.

School + Home

Home Activity Your child identified and read the words *live, out, people, who,* and *work.* Point to these words on the page. Have your child read each word and use it in a spoken sentence.

1.3.H.1 Identify at least 100 high-frequency words from a commonly used list.   Also 1.3.H.2.

© Pearson Education, Inc., 1

Name _____

Look at this book.
Write or circle your answers.

Who Works
at the Zoo?

by Kim Green

I. Who is the author of this book? **Kim Green**

2. What is the topic of this book?

   people in the ocean   (people at the zoo)   people on a ship

3. Why do you think Kim wrote this book?

   to make you laugh   to teach you tricks   (to tell facts)

Draw a picture that shows what this book is about.

4.

> **Children's drawings should relate
> to people working at a zoo.**

School + Home

Home Activity Your child learned to tell what a book might be about by figuring out why it was written. As you read various materials with your child, ask what he or she thinks each is about and why the author wrote it.

Name _____

 My Piano Teacher

Ms. Kindler teaches me to play piano. She shows me how to hold my fingers. She helps me read notes. She shows me the keys to press. She teaches me to play songs on the piano.

Key Features of an Explanation

• It tells about a person, idea, or thing.

• It helps people understand the topic.

Name _____

Circle the word for each picture.

 whisk

 chick

 itch

1.

wall (whale)

2.

shin (chin)

3.

(catch) cats

4.

wash (watch)

5.

ship (whip)

6.

chick (check)

7.

(patch) pass

8.

limp (chimp)

Pick a word to finish each sentence. **Write** the word on the line.

(graph)   grass

9. Henry made a mistake on his __**graph**__ .

(what)   want

10. He did not know __**what**__ to do.

 School + Home **Home Activity** Your child practiced reading words with digraphs *wh*, *ch*, and *tch* (letters that together stand for one sound). Have your child use each word above in a sentence.

© Pearson Education, Inc., 1

Name _____

Words with Long *i*

Spelling Words				
like	ride	smile	time	white
bike	dime	hide	ice	kite

Read the sentence. **Write** the words that rhyme.

They like the bike.

1. **like**   2. **bike**

The kite is white.

3. **kite**   4. **white**

Dad will use a dime this time.

5. **dime**   6. **time**

Write the missing word.

7. The **ice** makes me cold.

8. Did you walk or **ride** ?

9. She has a big **smile** on her face.

10. The cat likes to **hide** from me.

ice
hide
ride
smile

 School + Home

Home Activity Your child wrote words with the long *i* sound. Take turns with your child making up sentences containing the words. Spell the words aloud.

© Pearson Education, Inc., 1

Name _____

Special Titles

A **title** can come before the name of a person. A title begins with a capital letter. Titles can be abbreviations. Abbreviations end with a period (.).

Doctor Silva

Mrs. Faber

Mr. Gray

Write the title and the name correctly on the line.

I. miss oda

Miss Oda

2. captain bartz

Captain Bartz

3. dr. hashmi

Dr. Hashmi

4. ms. ford

Ms. Ford

School + Home

Home Activity Your child learned about special titles. Say the names and titles of adults your child knows, for example, *Dr. Kahn, Ms. Bell, Mr. Garcia.* Ask your child to identify and write the person's title.

© Pearson Education, Inc., 1

Name _____

Idea Web

Ms. Li

teaches drawing

reads picture books

My Art Teacher

teaches painting

has fun

School + Home

Home Activity Your child is learning about writing an explanation by telling what a teacher does. Talk with your child about jobs that people in a community do.

Name _____

W   w

Copy the words. Write the letters from left to right.

Wade   Wade   chop   chop

white   white   when   when

chime   chime   whim   whim

whine   whine   chill   chill

chin   chin   which   which

while   while   whale   whale

chase   chase   Will   Will

Did you write your letters from left to right?   Yes   No

© Pearson Education, Inc., 1

Home Activity Your child practiced writing words with *Ww*, *wh* and *ch*. Have your child choose three words from above and write the words one more time.

Name _____

Look at the map.

1. Circle the school.

2. Draw a box around the bank.

3. Underline the park.

4. Write the number of houses on block C.

5. Write the number of cars on the map.

© Pearson Education, Inc., 1

Home Activity Your child learned to use a map to gather information. Point out maps as you see them and challenge your child to point out places featured on the maps.

The White Kite

Long *i*: *i_e*	Consonant Digraphs *wh, ch, tch, ph*	High-Frequency Words
nice	white	the
line	checks	I
dives	patch	a
like	Ralph	is
		go

kite
quite
mile
smiles

Ralph calls Ann on the cell.

"I made a white kite!"

Ralph lets the kite go up.

It dips and dives.

"I like this kite!" Ralph tells Ann.

Decodable Story *The White Kite*
Target Skill Long *i*: *i_e*, Consonant Digraphs *wh, ch, tch, ph*

Ann checks the kite.

"It is small. But it is quite nice!"

Ralph smiles.

"The kite has a patch and a line.
It will go up a mile!"

Name _____

Words with Long *i*

Spelling Words				
like	ride	smile	time	white
bike	dime	hide	ice	kite

High-Frequency Words
who
work

Choose a word to finish the sentence.
Fill in the circle. **Write** the word.

1. The glass is full of ● ice ○ bike ○ dime.   **ice**

2. Be at ○ who ○ smile ● work on time.   **work**

3. Look at the ● kite ○ hide ○ like!   **kite**

4. It costs a ○ white ● dime ○ ice.   **dime**

5. ○ Work ○ Bike ● Who is coming   **Who**

6. You can ride my ● bike ○ ice ○ time.   **bike**

Read the word. **Write** the list word that means the opposite.

7. black **white**   8. show **hide**

9. walk **ride**   10. frown **smile**

Home Activity Your child used spelling words and high-frequency words to complete sentences. Have your child identify and write as many spelling words as possible to finish this sentence: *This is my_____.*

© Pearson Education, Inc., 1

Name _____

Special Titles

Tell about people who work in your community.
Use words from the box or your own words.
Use titles and names.

| teacher   mail carrier   police officer |
| doctor   vet   librarian |

Possible answer: Dr. Ted is

our vet. He helped our cat. Ms.

Ruiz teaches us to read.

Say other sentences about the people you chose.

Home Activity Your child learned how to use special titles in writing. Write these titles and names on paper: *mr jones, ms gold, dr novak.* Have your child explain what is wrong and write the titles and names correctly.

Name _____

Words with Long *i*

Write the list words in the puzzle.

Spelling Words

- like
- ride
- smile
- time
- white
- bike
- dime
- hide
- ice
- kite

Puzzle answers:
- 1. smile
- 2. time
- 3. dime
- 4. dice / ice

Draw lines to connect the words that rhyme. **Write** each word.

5. white
6. kite
7. ride
8. hide
9. like
10. bike

Home Activity Your child has been learning to spell words with long *i*. Draw large kite shapes. Have your child write long *i* words on them.

Name _____

Special Titles

Mark the sentence that uses the title and name correctly.

1. ⊗ Our doctor is Dr. Brown.
   ○ Our doctor is Dr. brown.
   ○ Our doctor is dr. Brown.

2. ○ My teacher is ms. Okada.
   ⊗ My teacher is Ms. Okada.
   ○ My teacher is Ms okada.

3. ○ Mr diaz brings our mail.
   ○ mr. Diaz brings our mail.
   ⊗ Mr. Diaz brings our mail.

4. ○ Our vet is Doctor tang.
   ○ Our vet is doctor Tang.
   ⊗ Our vet is Doctor Tang.

5. ○ miss Vale works at the library.
   ⊗ Miss Vale works at the library.
   ○ Miss vale works at the library.

6. ⊗ Mrs. Benik drives our bus.
   ○ Mrs. benik drives our bus.
   ○ mrs. Benik drives our bus.

Home Activity Your child prepared for taking tests on special titles. Together look through a newspaper or magazine. Have your child find and circle as many special titles as he or she can.

Name _____

Write the letters to make a word in each sentence.
Then read the story.

R **o** s **e** wanted to make soup. She didn't have a

b **o** n **e** . So she put a big st **o** n **e** in the pot. She

didn't have a st **o** v **e** . She made a fire outside her

h **o** m **e** . She hung the pot on a p **o** l **e** .

"I h **o** p **e** this will be good," Rose said.

_____

Circle the words that have the same long o sound as .

(clove)   bond   not   (poke)   stop   (spoke)

drop   lost   (vote)   son   color   (told)

 Home Activity Your child practiced reading words with the long o sound spelled o – e, such as *rope*. Work with your child to write a list of words that rhyme with *bone*. Repeat with *joke*.

Name _____

Read the words in the box.
Pick a word from the box to match each clue.
Write it on the line.

| down inside now there together |

1. not up

<u>**down**</u>

2. not here

<u>**there**</u>

3. not outside

<u>**inside**</u>

4. not then

<u>**now**</u>

5. not one here and one there

<u>**together**</u>

School + Home

Home Activity Your child identified and read the words *down, inside, now, there,* and *together.* Read one word aloud. Have your child point to it and use it in a sentence. Repeat with the other words.

Name _____

Write a number in each box to show the right order.
Then **act out** the story.

1. 2

2. 3

3. 1

Look at each picture.
Draw what will happen next.

4.

Artwork should reflect a completed nest in tree, maybe with eggs in it.

5.

Artwork should reflect a plant of some kind above ground.

Home Activity Your child learned about the order in which things happen in a story. After you read a story with your child, have your child tell you what happened first, next, and last in the story.

© Pearson Education, Inc., 1

Name _____

Time for Spines

It is late Monday night.

I go out for a bite.

It is dark out there.

But I am not scared.

Down comes the owl.

I will just bow

And stick out my spines

Because I am a porcupine.

Key Features of a Poem

· It can describe an event.

· The lines may rhyme.

Name _____

Read each sentence.
Write the contraction for the underlined words.

I <u>**do not**</u> think I can do this.   I <u>**don't**</u> think I can do this.

---

1. "I <u>**can not**</u> make a nest," said the little bird.   **can't**

2. "I <u>will</u> need help with the sticks," said the little bird.   **I'll**

3. "I <u>do not</u> think I can help," said the frog.   **don't**

4. "<u>You will</u> need a big bird to help you," said the frog.   **You'll**

5. "<u>I am</u> a big bird! I can help," said the big bird.   **I'm**

Home Activity Your child combined words to form contractions ending with *n't, 'm,* and *'ll.* Say a contraction aloud. Have your child tell you the two words that were combined to make the contraction. Repeat with the other contractions.

© Pearson Education, Inc., 1

Phonics Contractions   **269**

Name _____

Words with Long *o*

Spelling Words				
home	hope	rose	woke	those
bone	hose	joke	rode	stone

Write a list word for each clue.

1. You use it to water the grass. __hose__

2. You live here. __home__

3. It is a part of your body. __bone__

4. It makes you laugh. __joke__

5. It grows in a garden. __rose__

6. It hurts when it gets in your shoe. __stone__

Write the word that rhymes with each word.

7. smoke

__woke__

8. rope

__hope__

9. nose

__those__

10. code

__rode__

those
woke
hope
rode

Home Activity Your child wrote words with long *o*. Work together to think of other long *o* words. Take turns making up clues for the new words and guessing them.

Proper Nouns: Days, Months, Holidays

Days of the week begin with capital letters.

Sunday   Wednesday   Saturday

Months of the year begin with capital letters.

February   May   October

Holidays begin with capital letters.

Fourth of July   Memorial Day

Write the day, month, or holiday correctly on the line.

1. We learn about dinosaurs on monday.

   Monday

2. On thursday a man tells us about dinosaurs.

   Thursday

3. In november we put on a play about dinosaurs.

   November

4. The play tells about dinosaurs at thanksgiving!

   Thanksgiving

Home Activity Your child learned about days, months, and holidays. Say the names of a day, a month, and a holiday and help your child write each name. Be sure each name begins with a capital letter.

Name _____

Sequence

First

Mouse comes out of hole to eat berries that have dropped from a bush.

Next

Mouse sees a shadow of a big hawk over him and drops his berry.

Last

Mouse runs and jumps into his hole in time to miss the hawk.

© Pearson Education, Inc., 1

School + Home

Home Activity Your child is writing a poem about an animal. Have your child describe an animal.

Name _____

T t

An apostrophe takes the place of missing letters.

Copy the words. Slant all of your letters the same way.

isn't   isn't

can't   can't

Tom   Tom

don't   don't

didn't   didn't

I'm   I'm

you'll

we'll

they'll

I'll

wasn't   wasn't

won't   won't

Did you slant all of your letters the same way? | Yes | | No |

© Pearson Education, Inc., 1

Home Activity Your child practiced writing words with *Tt* and contractions with *'t*. Say the following words and have your child look at the list and write the contraction for them: *can not (can't); they will (they'll); is not (isn't); I am (I'm); can not (can't)*.

Name _____

Read the newsletter. **Answer** the questions.

The Neighborhood   March

Kids Help!
by Pam Ride

Jill and Sam went for a walk. Mrs. Bell's pet cat was out! The kids could see the cat. They ran to it. They got the cat. Mrs. Bell said, "You are good kids!" She gave them a hug.

---

1. What is the name of the newsletter?

The Neighborhood

2. What is the name of the story?

Kids Help!

3. What is the story about?

Kids get Mrs. Bell's cat.

Home Activity Your child learned to use a newsletter to get information. As you look at newsletters, newspapers, or magazines, point out the different kinds of type, such as bold or italic text. Discuss why the text looks different from the surrounding type.

Name _____

What Am I?

Long o: o_e		Contractions n't, 'm, 'll		High-Frequency Words	
nose	rope	I'm	can't	a	what
hole	pole	you'll	isn't	I	me
bone	globe			see	

I'm on a face.

I can't see, but I can smell.

What am I? (I'm a nose!)

I'm a ball that isn't in a game.

You'll see shapes and lines on me.

What am I? (I'm a globe!)

4

Decodable Story *What Am I?*
Target Skill Long *o*: *o_e*, Contractions *n't*, *'m*, *'ll*

You'll put me in the trash.

A pup puts me in a hole.

What am I? (I'm a bone!)

I'm tall and thin.

You'll see a flag and rope on me.

What am I? (I'm a pole!)

Name _____

Words with Long *o*

Spelling Words				
home	hope	rose	woke	those
bone	hose	joke	rode	stone

High-Frequency Words
there
together

Read about Fluff and Puff. **Write** the missing list words.

Fluff and Puff live by a big 1. **stone** . One day Pup

dug for a 2. **bone** . Pup 3. **woke**

Fluff and Puff. He entered their 4. **home** . Now

5. **those** bunnies needed a new home. They had

little 6. **hope** . Puff 7. **rode** on

Fluff's back as they looked. Then Pup poked up over a

8. **rose** bush. Pup pointed over 9. **there** . "I

found a perfect home. You can live by the bush

10. **together** .

Home Activity Your child used spelling words and high-frequency words in a story. Ask your child to write his or her own story, using some of the words.

Name _____

Proper Nouns: Days, Months, Holidays

Tell about a picnic, a fair, or a party.
Use the name of a month or holiday from the box

February	October	Valentine's Day
May	November	Fourth of July
July	December	Thanksgiving

Possible answer:

On the Fourth of July our town

has fireworks. People sit in

the park. They watch the sky.

The fireworks are great.

Home Activity Your child learned how to use days, months, and holidays in writing. Write these names on paper: *tuesday, april, memorial day.* Have your child explain what is wrong and write the names correctly.

278 Conventions Proper Nouns: Days, Months, Holidays

Name _____

Words with Long *o*

Write the words.

1. **stone**

2. **home**

3. **bone**

4. **rose**

Spelling Words

home
hope
rose
woke
those
bone
hose
joke
rode
stone

Write the missing letters. **Write** the list word.

5. h <u>o</u> p e   **hope**

6. th <u>o</u> s e   **those**

7. r <u>o</u> d e   **rode**

8. j <u>o</u> k e   **joke**

9. h <u>o</u> s e   **hose**

10. w <u>o</u> k e   **woke**

hope
woke
those
joke
rode
hose

School + Home

Home Activity Your child has been learning to spell words with long *o*. Have your child think of and write words that rhyme with *nose* or *cone*.

Proper Nouns: Days, Months, Holidays

Mark the sentence that uses the day, month, or holiday correctly.

1. ⊗ On Tuesday we collect cans.
   ○ On tuesday we collect cans.
   ○ On TuesDay we collect cans.

2. ○ A truck picks up the cans on friday.
   ⊗ A truck picks up the cans on Friday.
   ○ A truck picks up the cans on FRiday.

3. ○ The neighbors plant a garden in june.
   ○ The neighbors plant a garden in JUne.
   ⊗ The neighbors plant a garden in June.

4. ○ In august they pick the vegetables.
   ⊗ In August they pick the vegetables.
   ○ In AuGust they pick the vegetables.

5. ○ On memorial Day our town has a parade.
   ○ On Memorial day our town has a parade.
   ⊗ On Memorial Day our town has a parade.

6. ⊗ We watch fireworks on the Fourth of July.
   ○ We watch fireworks on the fourth of July.
   ○ We watch fireworks on the Fourth of july.

© Pearson Education, Inc., 1

Home Activity Your child prepared for taking tests on days, months, and holidays. Together look through a newspaper or magazine. Have your child find and circle any days, months, and holidays that he or she finds.

Name _____

Circle the word for each picture.

 <u>cu</u>be

1.

(mule)   mile

2.

tub   (tube)

3.

(cub)   cube

4.

(Pete)   pet

5.

tug   (tune)

6.

flat   (flute)

7.

(tub)   tube

8.

(hug)   huge

Find the word that has the same **long u** sound as .
Mark the ⬭ to show your answer.

9. ⬭ rut
   ⬭ rid
   ⬛ rule

10. ⬭ cut
    ⬛ cute
    ⬭ cup

© Pearson Education, Inc., 1

 School + Home

Home Activity Your child practiced reading words with the long *u* sound spelled *u – e*, such as *cube*. Write words from this page in a list. Say each word. Have your child point to the word and read it.

Name _____

Look at each picture.
Read the words.
Write the word on the line that best fits the picture.

1. find
around
_____ **find**

2. water
food
_____ **food**

3. around
under
_____ **around**

4. grow
find
_____ **grow**

5. water
under
_____ **under**

6. food
water
_____ **water**

© Pearson Education, Inc., 1

 Home Activity Your child identified and read the words *around*, *find*, *food*, *grow*, *under*, and *water*. Make up clues for the words on this page. Ask your child to identify the words. Challenge your child to think of some clues too.

282 **High-Frequency Words**

Name _____

Look at this book cover.
Circle or **write** your answers.

I. Who wrote this book? <u>**Bob Dog**</u>

2. What do you think this book will be about?

real dogs   (silly dogs)   a real trip

3. What do you think this book will be like?

(funny)   sad   full of facts

4. Why do you think the writer wrote this book?

to tell facts about dogs   to make you sad   (to make you laugh)

5. Would you want to read this book? Why or why not?

<u>Answers will vary. Children should give a reason for their choice.</u>

_____

_____

Home Activity Your child learned to tell what a book might be about by figuring out why it was written. As you read various materials with your child, have your child tell you what he or she thinks each is about and why the author wrote it.

Name _____

 Oh Deer!

Deer live in woods and fields. They eat all kinds of plants. Deer love apples. They eat apples that fall on the ground. In the winter they eat leaves. They nibble on branches. They use their paws to dig snow. Then they eat the nuts and plants they find. I like watching deer. They are beautiful.

Key Features of a Description

· It tells about real people or things.

· It uses descriptive words.

Name _____

Pick a word from the box to finish each sentence.
Add -ed to each word. **Write** it on the line.

┌───┐
│ call   walk   sniff   jump   rest   │
└───┘

1. They **jumped** rope together.

2. Pam **called** June.

3. They **walked** to the park.

4. They **rested** in the shade.

5. They **sniffed** the flowers.

Home Activity Your child practiced writing words ending in -ed, such as *patched*. Ask your child to read each word and use it in a sentence.

Name _____

Words with Long *u*

Spelling Words				
huge	June	rule	tube	use
cube	cute	flute	rude	mule

Write the list word that names the picture.
Write a list word that rhymes.

1. **mule**   2. **rule**

3. **tube**   4. **cube**

5. **flute**   6. **cute**

Read the meaning. **Write** the list word.

June
use
rude
huge

7. very big — **huge**

8. not polite — **rude**

9. a month — **June**

10. to work with something — **use**

Home Activity Your child spelled words with the long *u* vowel sound. Ask your child to name the two letters that occur in every word. (*u* and *e*)

Name _____

Singular and Plural Nouns

Many nouns add **-s** to mean more than one.

tree

trees

Draw a line from the noun to the correct picture.
Say a sentence for each plural noun.

1.

bug

bugs

2.

rocks

rock

3.

plants

plant

4.

log

logs

Home Activity Your child learned about plural nouns. Write the words *desk, lamp, chair, table,* and *cup.*
Have your child add *-s* to each word to make it mean more than one.

© Pearson Education, Inc., 1

Name _____

Idea Web

gnaw trees

eat bark and twigs

Beavers

build homes from trees

eat plants in water

© Pearson Education, Inc., 1

Home Activity Your child is learning how to describe animals in writing. Ask your child to describe things that one kind of animal does.

Name _____

D   d

Copy the words. Write the letters the correct size.

Duke	Duke
dusted	dusted
hushed	hushed
Deke	Deke
theme	theme
eve	eve

Dan	Dan
use	use
these	these
rushed	rushed
rocked	rocked
dashed	dashed

Did you write all of your letters the correct size? Yes   No

© Pearson Education, Inc., 1

Home Activity Your child practiced writing words with *Dd*, long *u*, long *e*, and words that end in *-ed*. Help your child find, read, and copy words from a favorite book.

Name _____

Read each index. **Answer** the questions.

My Book of Animals Index	
ants................................	3
fox	7
lion................................	10
zebra..............................	27

My Book of Plants Index	
blossom	4
flower	12
trees..............................	18
vines..............................	21

1. What can you read about on page 10? _____ **lions** _____

2. What page can you find out about vines? _____ **page 21** _____

Look at the words. **Place** them in the ABC order.

3. Where does **penguin** go?

fox _____ lion   lion **penguin** zebra

4. Where does **cactus** go?

blossom **cactus** flower   flower _____ tree

5. Where does **bird** go?

lion _____ zebra   ant **bird** fox

Home Activity Your child learned how to use alphabetical order to find information in an index. Ask your child to help you prepare a food-shopping list. Have your child alphabetize the list.

Duke the Mule

Long u / Long e	Inflected Ending –ed		High-Frequency Words	
Pete	yelled	jumped	a	he
cute	handed	helped	is	was
Duke			the	now
mule				
cube				

Pete has a cute pet.

His pet is Duke the mule.

In June the gate broke.

Duke handed Pete a wire.

Duke helped fix the gate!

4

Decodable Story *Duke the Mule*
Target Skill Long *u*, Long *e*; Inflected Ending -*ed*

Duke had a trick when he was small.

Pete yelled "Jump!"

Then Duke jumped past the cube.

Now Duke is big.

He walks places. He takes naps.

But Duke still has tricks.

Name _____

Words with Long *u*

Pick the word that finishes each sentence.
Write it on the line.

1. Put an ice **cube** in the glass.

2. I got to pet the **mule** .

3. You can **use** my pen.

4. School is out in **June** .

5. What a **cute** kitten!

6. Is there a **rule** about that?

7. This apple is **huge** !

8. Let's roll the ball down the **tube** .

9. Fill the glass with **water** .

10. The bug is **under** the rock.

© Pearson Education, Inc., 1

Spelling Words
huge
June
rule
tube
use
cube
cute
flute
rude
mule

High-Frequency Words
water
under

Home Activity Your child completed sentences by spelling words with long *u*. Write ___*u*___e and have your child fill in the blanks to spell a word.

Singular and Plural Nouns

Pretend you are in this park.
Tell about the plants and animals you see.

trees   flowers   squirrels   birds   rabbits
Possible answer:

I see one tree. There are four

flowers. The squirrels run.

The birds fly. The rabbits eat

the grass.

Home Activity Your child learned how to use plural nouns in writing. Read a story together. Ask your child to point out any words he or she sees that mean more than one.

© Pearson Education, Inc., 1

Name _____

Words with Long *u*

Spelling Words

huge	June	rule	tube	use
cube	cute	flute	rude	mule

Read the clue. **Write** the list word in the puzzle.

Across

3. after May

5. a pipe

6. animal

Down

1. a law

2. pretty

4. square box

Puzzle answers:
- ¹r
- ²c ³J u n e
- u l
- ⁴c ⁵t u b e
- ⁶m u l e
- b
- e

Circle the word that is spelled correctly.

7. (flute) flut   8. (rude) rood

9. huje (huge)   10. (use) yuse

Home Activity Your child has been learning to spell words with long *u*. Take turns with your child naming and spelling the words.

© Pearson Education, Inc., 1

Name _____

Singular and Plural Nouns

Mark the word that shows more than one.

I. Look at the two frogs.
○ the
○ Look
⊗ frogs

2. The bird eats the bugs.
⊗ bugs
○ eat
○ bird

3. The tree has three holes.
○ has
⊗ holes
○ tree

4. A bear is by the rocks.
○ bear
⊗ rocks
○ by

5. The squirrel hides the nuts.
⊗ nuts
○ squirrel
○ The

Home Activity Your child prepared for taking tests on plural nouns. Together look through a newspaper or magazine. Have your child find and circle as many plural nouns as he or she can.

Name _____

Help the bee get home.
Read each word.
Draw a line that goes past only the **long e** words.
Write the **long e** words on the lines.

b**ee**

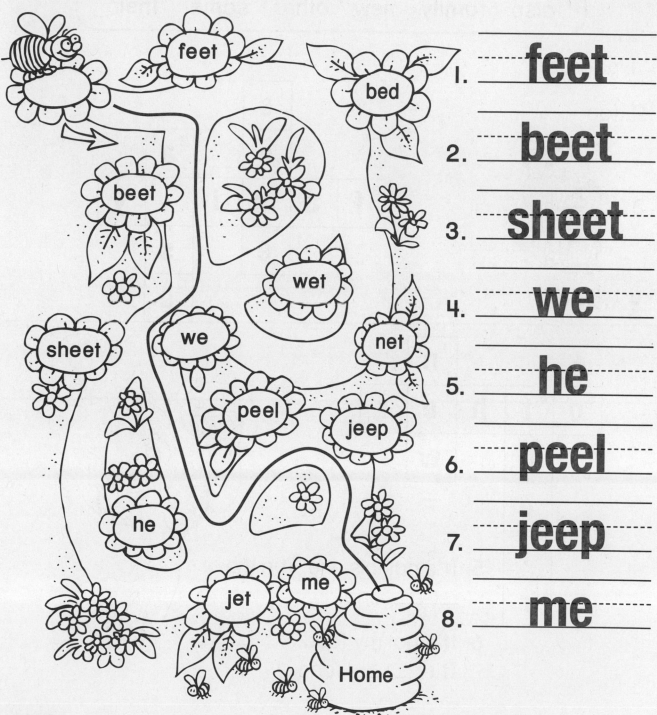

1. _____ feet
2. _____ beet
3. _____ sheet
4. _____ we
5. _____ he
6. _____ peel
7. _____ jeep
8. _____ me

Home Activity Your child practiced reading and writing words with the long e sound spelled e and ee, as in *he* and *jeep*. Have your child make a list of words that rhyme with *seed*. Repeat with *jeep*.

Name _____

Read the words in the box.
Pick a word from the box to match each clue.
Write the words in the puzzles.

> also   family   new   other   some   their

1. not a lot

2. too

3.

4. not old

¹s				²a	
o				l	
³f	a	m	i	l	y
e				s	
				o	

	⁴n			
⁵o	⁶t	h	e	r
t		n		
h		e		
e		w		
i				
r				

5. It's not this one. It's the
   _____ one.

6. It's not my food.
   It's _____ food.

Home Activity Your child identified and read the words *also, family, new, other, some,* and *their.* Help your child to make up a story or poem using these words. Work together to write the story or poem and read it to other family members.

Name _____

Look at both pictures.
Write sentences to tell how the pictures are the same and different.

Dee

Lee

Same
_____

1. **Possible answers:**

Dee and Lee have hats on.

2. **Dee and Lee are ants or about**

the same size.

Different
_____

3. **The hats are not the same.**

_____

4. **Dee has a flower in her hat.**

Lee doesn't.

5. **Lee has a flag. Dee doesn't.**

_____

© Pearson Education, Inc., 1

Home Activity Your child used pictures to tell how two things are alike and different. Point out two objects or two pictures to your child. Encourage your child to tell you how they are the same and how they are different.

Comprehension Compare and Contrast **299**

Name _____

Writing Prompt: Write a paragraph about how you help your community.

    I like to help in my community. I help at the park. On Saturday, I help grown-ups pick up. I help plant flowers in the spring. A bunch of us dress up the park for July 4th. Helping is fun!

Name _____

Circle the word for each picture.

ki**tt**en

1. ramp (**rabbit**)

2. (**button**) brake

3. (**dinner**) dent

4. base (**basket**)

5. (**helmet**) hello

6. (**napkin**) name

7. mask (**muffin**)

8. wall (**walnut**)

Draw a picture for each word.

9. mitten

Children's artwork should show a mitten.

10. picnic

Children's artwork should show a picnic.

Home Activity Your child read words with two syllables that have two consonants in the middle, as in *kitten*. Have your child choose five words from the page and use each word in a sentence.

Name _____

Words with Long e

Write the list word that names the picture.

1. **feet**   2. **tree**

Write e or *ee* to finish the word. **Write** the word.

3. **sh_e_**   **she**

4. **h_e_**   **he**

5. **gr_ee_n**   **green**

6. **m_e_**   **me**

7. **s_ee_**   **see**

8. **w_ee_k**   **week**

9. **w_e_**   **we**

10. **b_e_**   **be**

Home Activity Your child spelled words with the long e vowel sound. Ask your child to identify two different ways the sound is spelled in the list words. (e and ee)

© Pearson Education, Inc., 1

Name _____

Nouns in Sentences

A **noun** names a person, a place, an animal, or a thing. A noun can be in more than one place in a sentence.

Bees live in a **hive.**

Circle the noun in each sentence.
Draw and **color** a picture for each noun.
Say a sentence about your picture.   **Pictures will vary.**

1. The (sun) is warm.

| **should show a sun** |

2. Look at the (bee)

| **should show a bee** |

3. Where is the (flower)?

| **should show a flower** |

Home Activity Your child learned about nouns in sentences. Read a story together. Point to a sentence and have your child point to the nouns in the sentence. Continue with other sentences.

© Pearson Education, Inc., 1

Expository Paragraph
Top-Score Response

Focus/Ideas	A good expository paragraph tells important ideas about the main topic.
Organization	A good expository paragraph tells the ideas in an order that makes sense.
Voice	A good expository paragraph shows that you are interested in your topic.
Word Choice	A good expository paragraph uses words that describe.
Sentences	A good expository paragraph has sentences that are different lengths.
Conventions	A good expository paragraph has a noun in every sentence.

© Pearson Education, Inc., 1

Home Activity Your child is learning to write a paragraph about a topic such as insects. Ask your child to tell what kinds of insects live together in groups.

Name _____

B   b

Copy the words. Leave the correct space between the letters.

Bee   Bee   be   be

seed   seed   see   see

beet   beet   being   being

he   he   cheek   cheek

she   she   wheel   wheel

weep   weep   seem   seem

deep   deep   beef   beef

Did you leave the correct space between your letters? Yes No

Home Activity Your child practiced writing words with *Bb* and the long *e* sound as in *bee*. Have your child choose the long *e* words that begin with *b* and write them again.

Name _____

Answer the questions.

1. You are reading about bees this week. **Write** three other insects you would like to know more about.

    _____ _____ _____

    Responses will vary. Possible responses: ant, grasshopper, firefly

2. **Circle** the insect you want to know more about.
    Write two questions.

    _____

    Responses will vary. _____

    _____

    _____

3. **Circle** where you would find more information.

    globe   encyclopedia   computer

Home Activity Your child learned how to identify a topic and ask questions about the topic. Have a discussion with your child about which insects he or she would like to learn about. If possible, visit your local library to find books or other sources of reference about the topic.

© Pearson Education, Inc., 1

Name _____

Seeds

Long *e: e, ee*		VC/CV words	High-Frequency Words
he	needed	happen	to
be	weeds	problems	the
Lee	keep	insects	for
beet	weeks	basket	what
beets	see		watered
seeds	we'll		

Lee had seeds.

He needed to plant the seeds.

"What will the seeds be?" he asked.

Lee picked beets in six weeks.

"See the basket?" asked Lee.

"We'll get beets for lunch!"

Decodable Story *Seeds*
Target Skills Long e, VC/CV Words

Lee had problems.

Weeds came in.

Lee had to keep insects off.

Lee dug holes for the seeds.

He watered the seeds.

"What will happen?" he asked.

Name _____

Words with Long e

Spelling Words				
be	feet	he	see	we
green	me	she	tree	week

High-Frequency Words
some
family

Read the story. **Write** the missing list words.

1. Dad helped **me** build a house for the birds.

2. A bird came the next **week** .

3. Soon **she** laid some eggs.

4. Dad held me up to **see** them.

5. There were three **green** eggs.

6. I asked if **we** could take one inside.

7. Dad said that would not **be** wise.

8. I knew **he** was right.

9. Soon there will be **some** birds.

10. Now a bird **family** lives in the tree.

Home Activity Your child used spelling words to complete a story. Ask your child to use some of the list words in a story about an event in his or her life.

© Pearson Education, Inc., 1

Name _____

Nouns in Sentences

Bees are like a family.
Bees have special jobs.
Do people in your family have special jobs?
Write about the jobs.

Possible answer: Mom washes the car. Dad makes pancakes. My brother takes out the trash. My sister sets the table. I feed the dog.

Home Activity Your child learned how to use nouns when writing sentences. Take turns with your child telling about jobs that you do at home. Have your child identify any nouns either of you uses in your sentences.

Name _____

Words with Long e

Spelling Words				
be	feet	he	see	we
green	me	she	tree	week

Read the clue. **Write** the list word in the puzzle.

Down
1. seven days
2. large plant

Across
3. the color of grass
4. what you stand on

Circle the word that is spelled correctly. **Write** it.

5. b (be) **be**

6. (we) whe **we**

7. (he) hee **he**

8. mee (me) **me**

9. se (see) **see**

10. (she) shee **she**

 Home Activity Your child has been learning to spell words with long e. Draw a tree and have your child write words with long e in the branches.

Name _____

Nouns in Sentences

Mark the sentence that has a line under the noun.

1. ○ The bees <u>wake</u> up.
   ⊗ The bees <u>bees</u> wake up.
   ○ The bees wake <u>up</u>.

2. ○ Look <u>at</u> the hive.
   ○ Look <u>at</u> the hive.
   ⊗ Look at the <u>hive</u>.

3. ⊗ Jan likes sweet <u>honey</u>.
   ○ Jan likes <u>sweet</u> honey.
   ○ Jan <u>likes</u> sweet honey.

4. ○ The workers <u>get</u> mad.
   ○ The workers get <u>mad</u>.
   ⊗ The <u>workers</u> get mad.

5. ⊗ Where does <u>pollen</u> come from?
   ○ Where <u>does</u> pollen come from?
   ○ Where does pollen <u>come</u> from?

6. ○ A family <u>lives</u> together.
   ⊗ A <u>family</u> lives together.
   ○ A family lives <u>together</u>.

© Pearson Education, Inc., 1

School + Home

Home Activity Your child prepared for taking tests on nouns in sentences. Together read a simple newspaper or magazine article. Have your child circle as many nouns as he or she can find.

Name _____

 fr**y**

 bab**y**

Circle the word for each picture.

1. (puppy) put	**2.** flop (fly)	**3.** (muddy) meet	**4.** (bunny) ball
5. crib (cry)	**6.** sit (city)	**7.** (sky) skate	**8.** had (happy)

Circle the word to finish each sentence. **Write** it on the line.

9. I didn't eat breakfast and I was very ___**hungry**___ .
(hungry) money

10. After a day at the beach, my bathing suit was not ___**dry**___ .
(dry) my

© Pearson Education, Inc., 1

Home Activity Your child practiced reading words with the vowel sounds of *y* heard in *fry* or *baby*. Work with your child to put the above answers into two word lists—one of words in which *y* represents the long *e* sound (*baby*) and one in which it represents the long *i* sound (*fry*).

Phonics Vowel Sounds of *y* **313**

Name _____

Read the words in the box. **Pick** a word to finish each sentence.
Write it on the line.

| always becomes day everything |
| nothing stays things |

1. Jazzy likes to play all **day** .

2. **Nothing** can stop him!

3. He gets into **everything** .

4. He **always** makes a mess.

5. Jazzy **stays** in my room.

6. He hides **things** under the bed.

7. He rests when he **becomes** sleepy.

© Pearson Education, Inc., 1

School + Home

Home Activity This week your child identified and read the words *always, becomes, day, everything, nothing, stays,* and *things.* Use paper bag puppets to act out a scene using these new words.

314   **High-Frequency Words**

Name _____

Read the story. **Look** at the pictures.
Write 1, 2, 3 to show the right order.

1. It was a sunny day.
   Tim saw a slide.
   Tim went up the slide.
   Tim came down the slide.

2. **Read** the story.
   Write a sentence that tells what might happen next.
   Then **draw** a picture.

   Polly planted a seed.
   The seed grew into a plant.

_____

Possible answers: The plant becomes a flower.

Home Activity Your child learned about the order in which events happen in a story. As you read stories with your child, have your child tell you what parts of the story are important and the order in which they happen.

Name _____

 The Slide

Beth and Dave liked the park. They liked the big slide. They ran to the park. The big slide was gone!

"Wow!" Beth said. "Look at the new red slide over there!" Dave ran to it.

"It is a tube slide!" They slid down the new slide. They went zig and then zag. They liked it better than the old slide.

Key Features of a Realistic Story

· Characters and events seem real.

· The setting is like a real place.

· The story has a beginning, middle, and end.

Name _____

Circle a word to finish each sentence.
Write it on the line.

 n<u>o</u>

He (Hi)

1. "____**Hi**____," Luke said.

Hi (He)

2. ____**He**____ is little.

(No) Nod

3. ____**No**____ one can see him.

(so) see

4. She is ____**so**____ big.

---

bed (be)

5. He will grow to ____**be**____ big too.

Home Activity Your child practiced reading words with the long vowel pattern heard in *me*, *hi*, and *go*. Work with your child to make a list of words with the long *e* sound spelled *e* and the long *o* sound spelled *o*.

Phonics Syllable Pattern *CV* **317**

Name _____

Words with Vowel Sounds of *y*

Spelling Words
my   by   try   sunny   handy
fly   cry   lucky   silly   puppy

Write five list words that rhyme with **why.**

1. **my**   2. **by**   3. **try**

4. **fly**   5. **cry**

Write the missing word.

sunny   silly   lucky   handy   puppy

6. I have a **puppy** named Spot.

7. Spot likes **sunny** days.

8. My pup acts **silly** .

9. I am **handy** at taking care of Spot.

10. I am **lucky** to have a pup.

Home Activity Your child spelled words in which the long *e* or long *i* sound is spelled *y.* Ask your child to name the letter that is in every list word (*y*) and pronounce its sound (long *e* as in *puppy* or long *i* as in *fly*).

Action Verbs

A **verb** tells what someone or something does.

The girl **jumps**.

The boy **walks**.

Underline the verb in each sentence.
Say a sentence using each verb.

I. The plant <u>grows</u> in the sun.

2. Benny <u>helps</u> Ms. Torres.

3. Mr. Gray <u>works</u> in the neighborhood.

4. Benny <u>wishes</u> for a place to play.

5. Nai Nai <u>plays</u> by the slide.

6. Mom <u>walks</u> down the hall.

Home Activity Your child learned about verbs. Read a story together. Point to a sentence and have your child point to the verb in the sentence. Continue with other sentences.

Name _____

Story Chart

Title _____

Characters

Settings

Beginning

Middle

End of Story

Home Activity Your child can plan and then write a brief story. Have him or her tell what happens in the story.

Name _____

Y   y

Copy the words. Write the letters from left to right.

Yancy   Yancy   sky   sky

baby   baby   foggy   froggy

why   why   dusty   dusty

fly   fly   fry   fry

silly   silly   funny   funny

happy   happy   hilly   hilly

shy   shy   cry   cry

Did you write your letters from left to right? | Yes | | No |

Home Activity Your child practiced writing words with *Yy*. Have your child copy the following sentence as neatly as he or she can. *Why is the street hilly, bumpy, and rocky?*

Name _____

Jan is presenting a report about playgrounds.
Help her gather information.

builder   librarian   children

1. **Circle** who could help Jan find books about playgrounds.

2. **Put a diamond** around who could tell Jan how much it costs to build a playground.

3. **Put a box** around who could help Jan find out which playground toys are the most fun.

4. **Ask** two classmates which playground toy is their favorite. Write their answers.

_____   - - - - - - - - - - - - - - - -

Responses will vary.   _____

5. **Share** the information you gathered with your class.

Home Activity Your child learned about interviewing people as sources of information. Talk with your child about the people you rely on when you need information or answers. Ask you child to write two interview questions to ask a member of your family or community.

© Pearson Education, Inc., 1

Name _____

I'll Try It!

Vowel sounds of y:	Syllable Pattern CV	High-Frequency Words
my bumpy	hi hello	said
try Katy	tiny Bo	the
Jody picky	we no	is
funny Molly	me	to
mushy fluffy	be	
yucky yummy	so	

"Hi!" said Jody.

"Hello!" said the kids.

"We got muffins at the shop."

"Try my muffin," said Molly.

"It is fluffy and yummy."

"No," said Jody. "It is tiny!"

Decodable Story *I'll Try It!*
Target Skills Vowel Sounds of *y,* Syllable Pattern CV

"My muffin tastes funny.
It is so mushy," said Bo.

"Hand it to me. I'll try it!" Jody
yelled.

2

"My muffin is yucky.
It is bumpy," said Katy.

"Don't be so picky," Jody said.
"I'll try it!"

3

Words with Vowel Sounds of *y*

Spelling Words				
my	by	try	sunny	handy
fly	cry	lucky	silly	puppy

High-Frequency Words
things
always

Fill in the circle. **Write** the word.

1. Look at ○ fly ● my ○ handy   bike.

my

2. Today is a ● sunny ○ try ○ by   day.

sunny

3. Did you ○ silly ○ puppy ● cry?

cry

4. The song is ○ sunny ● silly ○ my.

silly

5. She was ● lucky ○ my ○ fly.

lucky

6. I ● try ○ lucky ○ sunny   very hard.

try

7. Bats can ○ silly ● fly ○ my.

fly

8. Do you have a ● puppy ○ cry ○ lucky?

puppy

9. I see many ○ sunny ○ fly ● things.

things

10. We ○ lucky ○ fly ● always   ride the bus.

always

School + Home

Home Activity Your child wrote spelling words to complete sentences. Read a sentence from this page. Ask your child to spell the list word.

© Pearson Education, Inc., 1

Name _____

Action Verbs

Write about things you do every day.
Use action verbs from the box or your own words.
Say several sentences and identify the verb.

eat	go	read
sleep	play	talk

Possible answer: I get up. I eat

breakfast. Next I go to school.

After school I call my mom.

Then I play with my friends.

Home Activity Your child learned how to use verbs in writing. Take turns with your child telling about things that you do every day. Have your child identify any action verbs either of you uses in your sentences.

Name _____

Words with Vowel Sounds of y

Write the letter **y**. Then write the word.

Spelling Words
my
by
try
sunny
handy
fly
cry
lucky
silly
puppy

1. fl**y**   fly
2. pupp**y**   puppy
3. cr**y**   cry
4. hand**y**   handy
5. sunn**y**   sunny
6. sill**y**   silly
7. luck**y**   lucky

Circle the words that rhyme with **fly**. **Write** the words.

sunny   (try)   handy   silly   (by)   (my)

8. try   9. by   10. my

Home Activity Your child has been learning to spell words in which the long *e* or long *i* sound is spelled *y*. Have your child underline list words with a long *i* sound and circle list words with a long *e* sound.

© Pearson Education, Inc., 1

Name _____

Action Verbs

Mark the sentence that has a line under the verb.

1. ○ <u>Benny</u> helps Mr. Gray.
   ⊗ Benny <u>helps</u> Mr. Gray.
   ○ Benny helps <u>Mr.</u> Gray.

2. ○ Mr. Gray lives in the <u>neighborhood</u>.
   ○ Mr. Gray <u>lives</u> in the neighborhood.
   ⊗ Mr. Gray <u>lives</u> in the neighborhood.

3. ⊗ We <u>grow</u> plants here.
   ○ We grow plants <u>here</u>.
   ○ We grow <u>plants</u> here.

4. ○ Nai Nai walks to the <u>meeting</u>.
   ⊗ Nai Nai <u>walks</u> to the meeting.
   ○ <u>Nai Nai</u> walks to the meeting.

5. ○ Benny sees the <u>blue</u> sky.
   ○ Benny sees the blue <u>sky</u>.
   ⊗ Benny <u>sees</u> the blue sky.

6. ○ <u>Ms. Torres</u> likes this place.
   ⊗ Ms. Torres <u>likes</u> this place.
   ○ Ms. Torres likes this <u>place</u>.

Home Activity Your child prepared for taking tests on verbs. Together read a short, simple newspaper or magazine article. Have your child circle as many action verbs as he or she can find.

Name _____

 ri**ng**

 ba**nk**

Circle the word for each picture.

1. sink (sing)

2. (skunk) skate

3. (sink) side

4. kink (king)

5. wink (wing)

6. (trunk) truck

7. (hand) hang

8. swim (swing)

Write the letters to finish the words for each sentence.

9. Please b r i **n g** me a d r i **n k**.

10. T h a **n k** you for the pretty r i **n g**.

11. I heard the horn h o **n k**.

School + Home **Home Activity** Your child read words that end with *ng* and *nk*. Say one of the words with *ng* or *nk* on this page and ask your child to say a word that rhymes with it. Then have your child say a word for you to rhyme.

Name _____

Read the words in the box.
Write a word to finish each sentence.

| any enough ever |
| every own sure were |

1. Do we have **e n o u g h** food?

2. Yes, I am **s u r e** we do.

3. Is **e v e r y** place set?

4. Yes, they **w e r e** set last night.

5. Do you need **a n y** flowers?

6. No, I have my **o w n** .

7. This will be the best day **e v e r** !

Home Activity This week your child identified and read the words *any, enough, ever, every, own, sure,* and *were.* Help your child make up a short story using some of these words. Then help your child to write down the sentences and draw a picture to go with his or her story.

© Pearson Education, Inc., 1

Name _____

Read the stories.
Circle the answer to each question.

Hens

Many hens are white.

But hens can also be red or black.

Some hens can fly a little.

Hens will roll in dust.

A hen can be a pet.

Pigs

Some pigs are pink.

But there are black pigs too.

A pig can be a pet.

Pigs will roll in the mud.

They do this when they are hot.

---

1. Which animal can fly?   (hen)   pig

2. Which animal rolls in mud?   hen   (pig)

3. Which animal can be black?   (hen and pig)   just hen

4. Which animal can be pink?   hen and pig   (just pig)

5. Which animal can be a pet?   (hen and pig)   just pig

Home Activity Your child compared and contrasted information in two stories. Have your child choose two birds and tell how the birds are alike and different.

© Pearson Education, Inc., 1

Name _____

What I Like About Ruby

I like when Ruby does not eat at first. Sometimes I don't want to eat. I know how she feels. My favorite part is when Ruby flies really high and far. That sounds like fun!

Key Features of Comments About a Story

• comments respond to the story

• tell what the writer thinks and feels

Name _____

Pick a word from the box to finish each compound word.
Write it on the line.
Draw a line to the picture it matches.

sidewalk

| ball   cakes   pole   set |

1. pan **cakes**

2. sun **set**

3. flag **pole**

4. base **ball**

Find the compound word.
Mark the ⬭ to show your answer.

5. ◯ sandy
   ⬬ sandman
   ◯ sanding

6. ◯ napkin
   ◯ happen
   ⬬ dishpan

Home Activity Your child read compound words—words formed by joining two or more other words. Walk around your house with your child and find things you see that are compound words (*toothbrush, hairbrush, bathtub*). Say each word and have your child identify the two words used to make the compound word.

Words with -ng, -nk

Look at each picture.
Write two list words that rhyme.

Spelling Words

bring
trunk
pink
bank
sang
wing
rink
blank
rang
sunk

1. **pink**

2. **rink**

3. **bring**

4. **wing**

5. **trunk**

6. **sunk**

Read the clue. **Write** the word.

7. You keep money in it.

7. **bank**

8. You did it to a bell.

8. **rang**

9. You did it to a song.

9. **sang**

10. You can write a word to fill it.

10. **blank**

Home Activity Your child spelled words ending in -ng and -nk. Have your child identify and spell each list word that ends with -nk.

Name _____

Verbs That Add -s

A **verb** can tell what one person, animal, or thing does. Add **-s** to show what is being done now.

Ruby **grows** bigger.   Ruby **spreads** her wings.

Complete each sentence.
Write the correct word on the line.
Say a sentence using each verb you wrote.

I. Pam _____ **reads** _____ a book.
        (reads, read)

2. Ned _____ **bakes** _____ a cake.
        (bake, bakes)

3. José _____ **rides** _____ a bike.
        (rides, ride)

4. Tina _____ **ties** _____ her shoes.
        (tie, ties)

© Pearson Education, Inc., 1

Home Activity Your child learned about verbs that add -s. Write the words *swim, run, walk, jump,* and *dance* on paper. Have your child add an -s to each word and then act out the word.

Name _____

Comments and Feelings

I Like When Ruby . . .	I Feel . . .	Because . . .
First swims	**Excited**	**It took me a long time to learn to swim, too.**
Flies high in the air	**Happy**	**Ruby must be having fun.**

School + Home **Home Activity** Your child can express ideas about a story. Ask your child's opinion about the story of Ruby the duck.

336 **Writing** Plan

© Pearson Education, Inc., 1

Name _____

K   k

Copy the words. Write the letters from left to right.

King	King	bring	bring
long	long	dunk	dunk
honk	honk	thank	thank
think	think	Kang	Kang
tank	tank	wing	wing
sang	sang	clank	clank
bank	bank	link	link

© Pearson Education, Inc., 1

Did you write your letters from left to right?   Yes   No

 School + Home

Home Activity Your child practiced writing words with *Kk* and words that end in *-nk* or *-ng*. Have your child write words that rhyme with *think*.

Name _____

Find these words in the Glossary of your student book.
Draw a picture to show what each word means.

1. feather
Children's drawings should illustrate the meaning of the word *feather*.

2. mother
Children's drawings should illustrate the meaning of the word *mother*.

3. night
Children's drawings should illustrate the meaning of the word *night*.

4. rain
Children's drawings should illustrate the meaning of the word *rain*.

5. father
Children's drawings should illustrate the meaning of the word *father*.

6. flew
Children's drawings should illustrate the meaning of the word *flew*.

© Pearson Education, Inc., 1

Home Activity Your child learned how to use a glossary to look up the meaning of words. Find a glossary in a book at home or at the library and work with your child to look up other words.

The King Sings a Song

Consonant Patterns *ng* and *nk*		Compound Words		High-Frequency Words	
think	king	upset	anything	a	do
pink	sing	inside	baseball	I	said
thanks	song	himself	hilltop	of	the
honk	long	cannot	rosebuds	to	

A king felt upset.

He sat inside by himself.

"I cannot think of anything to do," he said.

1

"I will sing with them," said the king.

"I will sing a long song.

Then I will be happy!"

4

Decodable Story *The King Sings a Song*
Target Skills Consonant Patterns -*ng* and -*nk*, Compound Words

"Get the baseball," said the queen.

"We can toss it on the hilltop."

"No, thanks," said the king.

"Take a walk," said the princess.

"See the rosebuds. Pet the pink pigs.

The geese will honk a song."

Name _____

Words with *-ng, -nk*

Spelling Words				
bring	trunk	pink	bank	sang
wing	rink	blank	rang	sunk

High-Frequency Words
every
sure

Write the missing **ng** or **nk**. **Write** the word.

1. Did you skate at the **ri nk** ?   **rink**

2. Put the bag in the **tru nk** .   **trunk**

3. The bell **ra ng** .   **rang**

4. The boat has **su nk** .   **sunk**

5. We clapped as he **sa ng** .   **sang**

6. I have a piggy **ba nk** .   **bank**

7. The bird hurt its **wi ng** .   **wing**

8. Did you paint it **pi nk** ?   **pink**

Write a high-frequency word to fit each clue.

9. no doubt **sure**   10. all **every**

Home Activity Your child wrote spelling words to complete sentences. Have your child say and spell the list words with *-ng*.

Name _____

Verbs That Add -s

Look at the picture.
Write a verb to finish each sentence.
Remember to add **-s** to each verb.
Add more words to the sentence if you want.

Possible answers:

The girl __makes a sand castle_____.

The boy __helps_____.

The dad __holds a shell_____.

The mom __reads_____.

Choose other verbs. **Say** a sentence for each verb.

Home Activity Your child learned how to use verbs that add -s in writing. Write these sentence frames on paper: *Dan* _____. *Anna* _____. Have your child write verbs that add -s to each sentence frame to make as many sentences as possible.

342 **Conventions** Verbs That Add -s

Name _____

Words with *-ng*, *-nk*

Unscramble the letters to make a list word.
Write the word.

Spelling Words
bring
trunk
pink
bank
sang
wing
rink
blank
rang
sunk

1. k i n p   1. **pink**

2. r n g a   2. **rang**

3. g n i w   3. **wing**

4. n r i k   4. **rink**

5. r t n k u   5. **trunk**

Write three list words that begin like .

6. **bring**   7. **bank**   8. **blank**

Write two list words that begin like .

9. **sang**   10. **sunk**

Home Activity Your child has been learning to spell words with *-ng* or *-nk*. Have your child spell a list word and use it in a sentence.

© Pearson Education, Inc., 1

Name _____

Verbs That Add -s

Mark the sentence that is correct.

1. ⊗ Amy plays a song.
   ○ Amys plays a song.
   ○ Amy plays a songs.

2. ○ Johns writes his name.
   ⊗ John writes his name.
   ○ John writes hiss name.

3. ○ Rosa makes one big pizzas.
   ○ Rosa makes one bigs pizza.
   ⊗ Rosa makes one big pizza.

4. ○ Daves runs a long race.
   ⊗ Dave runs a long race.
   ○ Dave runs a longs race.

5. ⊗ Kate learns a new game.
   ○ Kates learns a new game.
   ○ Kate learns a new games.

6. ○ Sam spells a hards word.
   ○ Sam spells a hard words.
   ⊗ Sam spells a hard word.

Home Activity Your child prepared for taking tests on verbs that add -s. Together read a short, simple newspaper or magazine article. Have your child find and circle as many verbs that end in -s as possible.

© Pearson Education, Inc., 1

Name _____

Greg fix**es** the bench**es**.

Add the ending.
Write the new word on the line.

Word	Ending	New Word
1. mix	+ -es	**mixes**
2. brush	+ -es	**brushes**
3. glass	+ -es	**glasses**
4. catch	+ -es	**catches**
5. dress	+ -es	**dresses**
6. bus	+ -es	**buses**
7. dish	+ -es	**dishes**
8. fox	+ -es	**foxes**
9. nut	+ -s	**nuts**
10. patch	+ -es	**patches**

© Pearson Education, Inc., 1

School + Home

Home Activity Your child added -*es* to verbs and nouns. Have your child use each new word in a sentence.

Name _____

Read the words in the box.
Pick a word to finish each sentence.
Write it on the line.

> away   car   friends   house   our   school   very

1. This is our new __**school**__ .

2. It is by my __**house**__ .

3. It is __**very**__ nice.

4. We go with our __**friends**__ .

5. They come in a __**car**__ .

6. My mom will walk __**away**__ . I will stay.

7. __**Our**__ teacher is inside.

Home Activity This week your child identified and read the words *away, car, friends, house, our, school,* and *very*. Use sock puppets to act out a new story using the words. Help your child write down the story you create.

© Pearson Education, Inc., 1

Name _____

Read the story.
Follow the directions.

Kate has a pet bird called Bing.

Her bird is green and red.

A bird is the best pet of all pets.

Bing plays with a bell.

Bing likes to talk.

I. **Write** two facts about the story.

Possible answers are: Bing is green and red.

Bing plays with a bell. Bing likes to talk.

2. **Write** the sentence from the story that is an opinion. **Explain** your answer.

A bird is the best pet of all pets. This sentence

cannot be proven.

School + Home **Home Activity** Your child has learned about fact and opinion. Discuss the difference between a fact and an opinion. A fact can be proven to be true; an opinion cannot be proven to be true. Have your child tell a fact and an opinion about his or her favorite food.

Name _____

Writing Prompt: Write a summary of your favorite story.

Ruby in Her Own Time is my favorite story. Ruby takes longer to do things than her brothers and sisters. She eats later. She swims later. But she flies farthest first. She leaves home. Then she comes back. She brings her new family.

Name _____

Circle the word for each picture.

 st<u>or</u>m

 sc<u>ore</u>

1.
(fork)   flick

2.
hen   (horn)

3.
(core)   conk

4.
(store)   stock

5.
con   (corn)

6.
(shorts)   shots

7.
port   (pot)

8.
(thorn)   tone

Find the word that has the same middle sound as .
Mark the ⬭ to show your answer.

9. ⬬ porch
    ⬭ poke
    ⬭ pole

10. ⬭ such
    ⬭ shut
    ⬬ shore

Home Activity Your child read words with *or* as in *storm* and *ore* as in *score*. Help your child make up a story using words with this vowel sound, such as *snore, horn, popcorn,* and *short.* Then have your child illustrate his or her story.

Name _____

Words with -es

Finish the list word. Then **write** the word that means more than one.

Spelling Words
fix
fixes
class
classes
wish
wishes
kiss
kisses
bus
buses

1. one b **us** _____

2. three **buses** _____

3. one k **iss** _____

4. three **kisses** _____

5. one w **ish** _____

6. three **wishes** _____

Write the missing word.

7. My **class** _____ has ten boys.

8. Sam **fixes** _____ clocks.

9. Do the music **classes** _____ meet here?

10. Can you **fix** _____ my bike?

classes
fix
fixes
class

Home Activity Your child spelled words that end with -es. Say a list word that does not end with -es. Ask your child to add -es and spell the new word.

Name _____

Verbs That Do Not Add -s

Do not add **-s** to a verb that tells what two or more people, animals, or things do now.

Meg and Jen **want** a new pet.

Circle the verb that shows more than one.
Say a sentence for each verb you wrote.

1. Meg and Jen (find) finds) some pets.

2. The pets (likes, like) to eat.

3. Pet stores (sell) sells) many pets.

Circle the correct verb. **Write** the verb on the line.

4. The girls _____ **see** _____ many pets.
   (see, sees)

5. The pets _____ **run** _____ to see us.
   (runs, run)

Home Activity Your child learned about verbs that do not add -s. Write this sentence beginning: *The children ____.* Then act out a verb, such as *swim, run, walk, jump,* and *dance.* Have your child say the verb to finish the sentence.

Name _____

Writing Rubric Summary
Top-Score Response

Focus/Ideas	A good summary tells important information.
Organization	A good summary tells the ideas in the correct order.
Voice	A good summary shows that you understand the ideas.
Word Choice	A good summary uses words that describe and show time order.
Sentences	A good summary uses complete sentences.
Conventions	A good summary uses subjects and verbs that go together.

Home Activity Your child is learning how to write a short summary of a story. Read a short story together, and ask you child to briefly retell what happens in the story.

Name _____

R   r

Copy the words. Write the letters the correct size.

Rory   Rory   shore   shore

for   for   corn   corn

store   store   more   more

chore   chore   short   short

storm   storm   sore   sore

born   born   fort   fort

torn   torn   fork   fork

Did you write all of your letters the correct size?   Yes   No

Home Activity Your child practiced writing words with *Rr*, *or*, and *ore*. Have your child read and write any five words from the list one more time.

Name _____

Read Alex's chart with facts he has gathered.
Help him revise his topic.

Facts About	
Mammals	**Reptiles**
have hair on their bodies	have dry skin and no hair
babies born alive	alligators, crocodiles, turtles, snakes
bears, cats, whales, people	

1. Alex's topic is "Facts about Mammals and Reptiles." Does he have the right information to write about that topic? Why or why not?

   Possible response: Yes, he has a chart with facts about mammals and reptiles.

2. What additional fact about reptiles might Alex want to find?

   how reptile babies are born

3. Alex wants to revise his topic. Use Alex's chart to choose the topic.

   (How mammals and reptiles are alike and different)

   How mammals and reptiles live

4. Why is that a better topic for Alex?

   Possible response: Alex's facts are mostly about how mammals and reptiles are alike and different.

© Pearson Education, Inc., 1

Home Activity Your child learned how to review and revise topics. Choose a topic that is of interest to your child. Ask your child to share some facts about this topic with you. Then, using a reference source such as a computer or encyclopedia, read with your child about the topic. Have your child revise his or her list based on the results of your research.

© Pearson Education, Inc., 1

Six Wishes

Ending -es and plural -es	r-controlled or and ore		High-Frequency Words	
fetches	porch	chores	a	said
hatches	for	snored	the	of
wishes	horn	snores	I	is
foxes	more			
buses				
boxes				

Elf sat on the porch.

"I will grant six wishes," said Elf.

"This will be fun," said the foxes.

1

Funny Fox snored. Elf got a horn.

"I will grant this last wish."

No more snores!" said Elf.

4

Decodable Story *Six Wishes*
Target Skills Endings *-es*; Plural *-es*; *r-*controlled *or, ore*

Franny Fox wished for a pet that fetches.

"Can I get a hen that hatches fancy eggs?" asked Freddy Fox.

Sleepy Fox wished for buses.

Winky Fox wished for boxes of dishes.

"My wish is no more chores," said Franky Fox.

Words with -es

Spelling Words				
fix	fixes	class	classes	wish
wishes	kiss	kisses	bus	buses

High-Frequency Words
friends
very

Read about a wish. **Write** the missing list words.

1. I __wish__ I could visit my aunt.

2. I would go by __bus__ .

3. I might need to ride on two or three __buses__ .

4. My aunt __fixes__ hair in her shop.

5. She would __fix__ my hair.

6. She teaches art __classes__ , too.

7. I could go to a __class__ .

8. I would give my aunt a big __kiss__ .

9. She would give me a __very__ big kiss.

10. I hope my __friends__ meet her.

Home Activity Your child wrote spelling words to complete a story. Ask your child to write about a wish, using some of the list words.

© Pearson Education, Inc., 1

Verbs That Do Not Add -s

Pretend you see two new girls at school.
Write about what you do.
Write about what they do.
Begin your sentences with <u>we</u> and <u>they</u>.

Possible answer: We tell the girls our names. We show them their room. They thank us.

_____

_____

Home Activity Your child learned how to use verbs that do not add -s in writing. Point to pictures that show more than one person, animal, or thing. Ask: *What do the (children, birds, etc.) do?* Have your child write the answer to the question.

Name _____

Words with -es

Read the clues. Write the list words.

Spelling Words
fix
fixes
class
classes
wish
wishes
kiss
kisses
bus
buses

1. It rhymes with **Gus**.

bus

2. It rhymes with **glass**.

class

3. It rhymes with **fishes**.

wishes

4. It rhymes with **dish**.

wish

5. It rhymes with **mix**.

fix

6. It rhymes with **miss**.

kiss

Add -es. Write the new word in the puzzle.

Down
7. bus
8. fix

Across
9. kiss
10. class

7. b
u
s
e
s

8. f
i
x
e
s

9. k i s s e s

10. c l a s s e s

© Pearson Education, Inc., 1

School + Home

Home Activity Your child has been learning to add -es to words. Have your child write a list word that ends with -es. Then have your child cross out -es to make a different list word.

Name _____

Verbs That Do Not Add -s

Mark the sentence that is correct.

1. ○ Ann and Pat walks to a pet store.
   ○ Ann walk to a pet store.
   ⊗ Ann and Pat walk to a pet store.

2. ⊗ The girls like their new pets.
   ○ The girls likes their new pets.
   ○ The girl like their new pets.

3. ○ Their pet live in a box.
   ⊗ Their pets live in a box.
   ○ Their pets lives in a box.

4. ⊗ Ben and Vic talk to the girls.
   ○ Ben talk to the girls.
   ○ Ben and Vic talks to the girls.

5. ○ The boy tell about the new pet.
   ⊗ The boys tell about the new pet.
   ○ The boys tells about the new pet.

6. ○ Pat like the mice.
   ○ Ann and Pat like the mice.
   ⊗ Ann and Pat like the mice.

Choose other verbs. **Say** a sentence with each verb.

Home Activity Your child prepared for taking tests on verbs that do not add -s. Together read a paragraph from a newspaper or magazine article. Have your child find and circle verbs that do not end in -s.

Name _____

Dan is mop**ping** up the mess.
The mess is mop**ped** up.

Add -ed and **-ing** to each word.
Write the new words on the lines.

	Add -ed	Add -ing
1. nap	napped	napping
2. pat	patted	patting
3. nod	nodded	nodding
4. jog	jogged	jogging
5. wag	wagged	wagging
6. stop	stopped	stopping
7. pet	petted	petting
8. drop	dropped	dropping
9. clap	clapped	clapping
10. plan	planned	planning

School + Home **Home Activity** Your child practiced writing words that end in -ed and -ing. Together with your child make up a story using the words above.

Name _____

Circle a word to finish each sentence.
Write it on the line.

how

1. We have a _____ **few** _____ to take back.

---

afraid ⬭ read

2. We _____ **read** _____ them all and came for new ones.

⬭ again ⬭ few

3. Can we get some _____ **again** _____ ?

---

soon ⬭ how ⬭

4. We can read _____ **how** _____ to plant flowers.

⬭ afraid ⬭ few

5. I am _____ **afraid** _____ this is not the best one.

---

afraid ⬭ soon ⬭

6. My mom will be here _____ **soon** _____ .

Home Activity This week your child identified and read the words *afraid*, *again*, *few*, *how*, *read*, and *soon*.
Make some flash cards and have your child practice reading the words.

Name _____

Read the story.

Circle or write the answer to each question.

Skunks are always black and white.

Some skunks are black with white spots.

Skunks eat at sunset.

Skunks are good at digging.

They dig to find bugs to eat.

---

1. What is this story about?

   bugs   (skunks)   sunsets

2. Why do you think the writer wrote this story? Explain your answer.

   to make you laugh   to make you sad   (to tell facts)

   Possible response: The author likes skunks.

3. What are two things the story tells about skunks?

   Possible answers are: Some skunks are black with

   white spots. Skunks eat at sunset. Skunks are good

   at digging. Skunks dig to find bugs to eat.

Home Activity Your child read an informational story and figured out why it was written. Read a funny story with your child and talk about why the author wrote it.

Name _____

Lists

Things That Helped

Toad planted the seeds in the ground.

Toad let the seeds get rain.

Things That Did Not Help

Toad told the seeds to grow.

Toad read a story to the seeds.

Key Features of a List

- has words or sentences written one below the other

- can have a heading

Name _____

Circle the word for each picture.

f<u>ar</u>m

1.	2.	3.	4.
(arm) am	band (barn)	core (car)	far (jam)

5.	6.	7.	8.
duck (dark)	(party) patty	(cart) cork	cord (card)

Find the word that rhymes with ☆.
Mark the ⬭ to show your answer.

9. ⬭ form
   ⬛ far
   ⬭ for

10. ⬛ tar
    ⬭ torn
    ⬭ trap

 Home Activity Your child read words with *ar* as in *farm*. Help your child make up a story about a car trip. Encourage your child to use words with *ar* that have the same vowel sound as *car*.

Name _____

Words with -ed

Write the list word to finish the chart.

Spelling Words

	Base Word	-ed Word
1.	ask	asked
2.	drop	dropped
3.	help	helped
4.	plan	planned

Spelling Words:
ask
asked
plan
planned
help
helped
drop
dropped
call
called

Read the clues. Write the list word.

It rhymes with
It starts with **pl.**

It rhymes with
It starts with **c.**

It rhymes with
It starts with **j.**

5. plan   6. call   7. jog

Write the list word that tells what happened in the past.

8. We can <u>ask</u> for paper. We **asked** for paper.

9. I will <u>call</u> my friends. I **called** my friends.

10. He can <u>help</u>. He **helped** .

 School + Home **Home Activity** Your child spelled words that do and do not end with -ed. Say a list word Toad that does not end with -ed. Have your child say and spell the corresponding -ed word.

366 **Spelling** Words with -ed

Name _____

Verbs for Past and for Future

A verb can tell what happened in the past. Some verbs that tell about the past end with **-ed.** A verb can tell what happens in the future. It can begin with **will.**

Frog **walked.** (past)   Frog **will walk.** (future)

Read each word in the box. **Write** the word under *The Past* if it tells about the past. **Write** the word under *The Future* if it tells about the future. **Say** each verb you wrote in a sentence.

> will tell   liked   jumped
> helped   will play   will ask

The Past

1. __liked__

2. __jumped__

3. __helped__

The Future

4. __will tell__

5. __will play__

6. __will ask__

© Pearson Education, Inc., 1

Home Activity Your child learned about verbs for the past and for the future. Write the words *talk, laugh,* and *yell* on paper. Have your child add *-ed* or *will* to make a verb for the past and a verb for the future.

Name _____

Idea Web

Things That Helped

Planted seeds

Left them alone

Things That Did Not Help

Read poems

Played music

Home Activity Your child can write about the actions of characters in stories. Share a memory about a story you have heard or read with your child and why characters did things.

© Pearson Education, Inc., 1

Name _____

C

c

Copy the words. Leave the correct space between your letters.

Carl   Carl

Cal   Cal

car   car

cape   cape

barn   barn

harm   harm

start   start

jar   jar

chart   chart

star   star

part   part

bark   bark

card   card

dark   dark

Did you leave the correct space between your letters? Yes No

Home Activity Your child practiced writing words with *Cc* and *ar*. Have your child find three words from the list that rhyme with *far* and write them one more time. (*car, jar, star*)

Name _____

We use our eyes to gather information.
Look at the storm. **Write** what you see.

A Storm

1. Where does the rain come from? _____ **clouds** _____

2. How many bolts of lightning do you see? _____ **one** _____

3. Do you see a cloud? Circle a cloud.

4. Think about what you know about
storms. What part makes you wet? _____ **rain** _____

5. **Write** a question that you would ask a weather reporter
about storms.

Questions will vary.

Home Activity Your child made observations from a natural source and recorded those observations. As you interact with your child this week, point out what can be observed in our homes and in nature.

© Pearson Education, Inc., 1

Name _____

The Cart

Adding endings-double final consonants		r-controlled ar		High-Frequency Words	
humming	grabbed	Arty	started	a	said
running	stepped	cart	Marny	I	to
quitting	stopped	park	barked	the	is
getting	hugged	yard	bark		
begged					

Dad made Arty a black cart.

"Can I drive at the park?" begged Arty.

"No. Drive in the yard," said Dad.

"I'm not quitting," Arty yelled to Dad.

"Marny is getting in the cart."

This time he had a happy bark!

Decodable Story *The Cart*
Target Skills Adding Endings, *r*-controlled *ar*

Arty began humming.
He grabbed the wheel and
stepped on the gas.
The cart started!

2

Marny the dog began running
beside Arty.
He barked a sad bark.
Arty stopped the cart and
hugged Marny.

3

Name _____

Words with -ed

Spelling Words				
ask	asked	plan	planned	help
helped	drop	dropped	call	called

High-Frequency Words
again
soon

Write the missing list words.

1. He __asked__ if I could come.

2. We have not __planned__ a trip.

3. She __dropped__ a pen.

4. Has your mom __called__ you back home?

5. Jack __helped__ clean.

6. Did you __call__ your dog?

7. I will __ask__ for more.

8. Tom likes to __drop__ and run.

9. Liz will have a plan __soon__ .

10. I jogged on the path __again__ .

Home Activity Your child wrote words that end with -ed and their base words. Ask your child to find two words in which the final consonant was doubled before adding -ed (plan/planned, jog/jogged).

© Pearson Education, Inc., 1

Verbs for Past and for Future

In the past you were a baby.
Tell about things you did then.

Possible answer: I crawled. I stayed in a crib. I played with baby toys.

Now you are in first grade.
Tell about things you will do in the future.

Possible answer: I will read. I will talk with friends. I will play baseball.

Say the verbs you wrote. **Use** each verb in a sentence.

Home Activity Your child learned about verbs for the past and for the future. With your child, look through a family photo album. Talk about what you were doing then using verbs for the past. Talk about what you might be doing in the future.

Name _____

Words with -ed

Read the base word. **Write** the -ed word in the puzzle.

Across

2. drop   4. call
5. help

Down

1. ask
3. plan

	¹a
	s

²d r o p ³p e d

k

Down

l
⁴c a l l e d
e
d

n

n

⁵h e l p e d

d

Circle the word that is spelled correctly.

6. (plan)   plann   7. asc   (ask)

8. cal   (call)   9. (help)   halp

10. (drop)   dropp

Home Activity Your child has been learning to add -ed to base words. Have your child write a list word that ends with -ed. Then have your child cross out the ending (-ed or consonant + -ed) to find the base word.

© Pearson Education, Inc., 1

Verbs for Past and for Future

Mark the sentence that is correct.

1. ⊗ Last week Frog planted seeds in the garden.
   ○ Last week Frog plants seeds in the garden.
   ○ Last week Frog plant seeds in the garden.

2. ○ Soon Toad plant seeds.
   ⊗ Soon Toad will plant seeds.
   ○ Soon Toad planted seeds.

3. ⊗ Tomorrow the seeds will start to grow.
   ○ Tomorrow the seeds started to grow.
   ○ Tomorrow the seeds start to grow.

4. ○ Yesterday Frog will shout at Toad.
   ⊗ Yesterday Frog shouted at Toad.
   ○ Yesterday Frog shouts at Toad.

5. ⊗ Last week the sun shined.
   ○ Last week the sun shine.
   ○ Last week the sun shines.

6. ○ Tomorrow Toad looks at his garden.
   ○ Tomorrow Toad looked at his garden.
   ⊗ Tomorrow Toad will look at his garden.

Say sentences using verbs for the past and for the future.

Home Activity Your child prepared for taking tests on verbs for the past and for the future. Together read part of a newspaper or magazine article. Have your child find verbs that tell about the past or the future.

© Pearson Education, Inc., 1

Name _____

h**er**   b**ir**d   s**ur**f

Circle the word for each picture.

1.

short (**shirt**)

2.

(**clerk**) click

3.

(**curl**) chill

4.

barn (**burn**)

5.

(**fern**) fan

6.

(**skirt**) skit

7.

fist (**first**)

8.

(**stir**) store

Find the word that has the same vowel sound as .
Mark the ⬭ to show your answer.

9. ⬭ hard
   ⬭ hut
   ⬛ hurt

10. ⬭ torn
   ⬛ turn
   ⬭ tune

 Home Activity Your child read words spelled with *er, ir,* and *ur* that have the same vowel sound as *bird*. Help your child make up rhymes using words with this vowel sound spelled *er, ir, ur*. For example, *You can't wear that shirt. It is covered in dirt!*

Name _____

Read the words in the box.
Pick a word to finish each sentence.
Write the words in the puzzles.

push visit wait

1. We'll _____ our friends soon.

2. They will _____ us on the swings.

3. I can not _____ !

done know

4. I _____ we will do well!

5. We will try to win. We will be happy when we are _____ .

Home Activity Your child identified and read the words *done, know, push, visit,* and *wait.* Write the words on a sheet of paper. Give your child a clue for each word. Then have him or her guess the word and point to it.

© Pearson Education, Inc., 1

Name _____

Read the story.
Follow the directions.

Hand drums are fun to play.

You don't use sticks.

You tap on the top of the drum with your hands.

In the past, people made hand drums from trees.

They made the tops of the drums with animal skins.

I. **Write** two facts from the story.

Possible answers are: You tap on the top of the drum with your hands. In the past, people made hand drums from trees. People made the tops of the drums with animal skins.

2. **Write** the sentence from the story that is an opinion.

Hand drums are fun to play.

© Pearson Education, Inc., 1

Home Activity Your child has learned about fact and opinion. Review the difference between a fact and an opinion. A fact can be proven to be true; an opinion cannot be proven to be true. Have your child tell a fact and an opinion about one of the seasons of the year.

Name _____

The bird is yellow in summer.   Now the bird is brown. It changed color in winter.

Key Features of Captions and Pictures

• Captions tell about what pictures show.

• Many captions are sentences.

Name _____

Pick a word from the box that means the same as each pair of words. **Write** it on the line.

<u>She is</u> tall.
<u>She's</u> tall.

| he's | it's | I've | that's | they're |
| they've | we're | we've | you're | you've |

I. I + have

I've

2. we + are

we're

3. it + is

it's

4. that + is

that's

5. you + have

you've

6. they + have

they've

7. we + have

we've

8. he + is

he's

9. they + are

they're

10. you + are

you're

Home Activity Your child practiced making contractions with *'s, 've,* and *'re.* Read each contraction on this page aloud. Challenge your child to use each one in a sentence. Then work together to write each sentence.

Name _____

Words with *er, ir, ur*

Spelling Words				
her	first	bird	girl	burn
were	shirt	fur	hurt	sir

Read the clues. **Write** the list word.

It starts like

It rhymes with **bur.**

1. **fur**

It starts like

It rhymes with **dirt.**

2. **shirt**

It starts like

It rhymes with **turn.**

3. **burn**

Write the list word that means the opposite.

4. last **first**

6. heal **hurt**

5. boy **girl**

7. him **her**

Write the missing list word.

sir	were	bird

8. We saw a **bird** .

9. May I help you, **sir** ?

10. We **were** at a pond.

Home Activity Your child spelled words with *er, ir,* and *ur.* Have your child circle these letter combinations in the list words.

Name _____

Verbs: *Am, Is, Are, Was, Were*

The words **am, is,** and **are** tell about now. Use **am** or **is** to tell about one. Use **are** to tell about more than one.

I **am** big.

It **is** little.

They **are** tiny.

The words **was** and **were** tell about the past. Use **was** to tell about one. Use **were** to tell about more than one.

It **was** hungry.

They **were** hungry.

Circle the verb in each sentence. **Write Now** if the sentence tells about now. **Write Past** if the sentence tells about the past.

1. I ⟨was⟩ an egg.   **Past**

2. I ⟨am⟩ a caterpillar.   **Now**

3. They ⟨are⟩ caterpillars.   **Now**

4. They ⟨were⟩ eggs.   **Past**

5. The change ⟨is⟩ amazing.   **Now**

Home Activity Your child learned about *am, is, are, was,* and *were*. Read a story with your child. Have your child point out the verbs *am, is, are, was,* and *were* in the story and tell whether the sentence tells about now or the past.

Name _____

Picture Plan

Picture 1

Caption: **Apple tree in spring**

Picture 2

Caption: **Apple tree in fall**

Home Activity Your child is writing captions. Together, look at picture in children's books and read captions.

384 **Writing** Plan

Vv   An apostrophe takes the place of missing letters.
            →' 've

Copy the words. Write the letters from left to right.

Val   Val   Van   Van

I've   I've   hive   hive

vine   vine   we've we've

you've you've   vest   vest

five   five   Vicky Vicky

haven't haven't   dive   dive

could've could've   they've they've

Did you write your letters from left to right? [Yes] [No]

Home Activity Your child practiced writing words with *Vv* and contractions with *'ve.* Say the words that form some contractions on this page, and have your child write the contractions one more time: *I have (I've); you have (you've); we have (we've); they have (they've); could have (could've).*

Name _____

We use our eyes to gather information.
Look at the park. **Write** what you see.

1. What is the man doing? **feeding the birds**

2. Do you see things that fly? **Circle** them.

3. How many people do you see in the park? **three**

4. **Write** two questions that you would ask the people in the park.

_____

Questions will vary. _____

_____

_____

© Pearson Education, Inc., 1

 Home Activity Your child made observations from a natural source and recorded those observations. As you interact with your child this week, point out what can be observed in our homes and in nature.

Helping Mom

r-controlled er, ir, ur	Contractions	High-Frequency Words	
Fern	bird	I've	said	to
her	stir	I'll	the	play
shirts	fur	can't	I	
skirts	Kurt	we're	you	
dirty	burn	you'll	is	

"I've got sixteen jobs on my list," said Mom.

"I'll need all the help I can get."

1

Fern and Kurt grinned.

"We're glad to help.

Then you'll get to play a game with us!"

4

Decodable Story *Helping Mom*
Target Skills *r*-controlled *er, ir, ur*; Contractions

"Fern, will you hang up these shirts and skirts?" asked Mom.

"Will you brush the dog? Her fur is dirty."

"Kurt, will you feed the bird?" asked Mom.

"Will you stir the gumbo? We can't let it burn."

Name _____

Words with *er, ir, ur*

Circle the word that is spelled correctly. Write it.

1. I like your ____.
   shert (shirt) shurt
   ___shirt___

2. I knew where you ____.
   (were) wir wure
   ___were___

3. Meet the new ____.
   gerl (girl) gurl
   ___girl___

4. Let the candle ____.
   bern birn (burn)
   ___burn___

5. Judy said, "Yes, ____."
   ser (sir) sur
   ___sir___

6. Look at the ____.
   berd (bird) burd
   ___bird___

7. Can I be ____?
   ferst (first) furst
   ___first___

8. His dog has black ____.
   fer fure (fur)
   ___fur___

9. Are you ____?
   dun dune (done)
   ___done___

10. Let's ____ our friends.
    (visit) visot visat
    ___visit___

Spelling Words

her
first
bird
girl
burn
were
shirt
fur
hurt
sir

High-Frequency Words

visit
done

Home Activity Your child used spelling words in sentences. Help your child make up a new centence for each spelling word.

Verbs: *Am, Is, Are, Was, Were*

Look at the picture.
Tell about what you see.
Use am, is, are, was, or **were.**

Possible answer: I am looking at a picture. Some leaves are there. One bird is on a leaf. The bird was flying. Were other birds in the tree?

Read the question. **Change** the words to write the answer.
Is that a bird?

That is a bird.

Home Activity Your child learned how to use *am, is, are, was,* and *were* in writing. Write these sentence frames on paper: *Today I ____ happy. Now he ____ happy. Yesterday she ____ happy. Now they ____ happy. Yesterday we ____ happy.* Have your child complete the sentences with *am, is, are, was,* and *were.*

Name _____

Words with *er, ir, ur*

Spelling Words				
her	first	bird	girl	burn
were	shirt	fur	hurt	sir

Use this code. **Write** the words.

1. hurt   2. sir   3. shirt

4. her   5. first   6. fur

Draw a line through the word that does not match.
Then **write** the word that matches.

7. were   ~~where~~   were   **were**

8. bird   bird   ~~bid~~   **bird**

9. ~~grill~~   girl   girl   **girl**

10. burn   ~~turn~~   burn   **burn**

Home Activity Your child has been learning to spell words with *er, ir,* and *ur.* Write a list word, but replace the letter before *r* with a blank (b__rd). Ask your child to correctly fill in the blank.

Verbs: *Am, Is, Are, Was, Were*

Mark the sentence that is correct.

1. ⊗ The caterpillar is in the tree.
   ○ The caterpillar am in the tree.
   ○ The caterpillar are in the tree.

2. ○ The bees is on the flowers.
   ○ The bees was on the flowers.
   ⊗ The bees are on the flowers.

3. ○ One bird were yellow.
   ⊗ One bird was yellow.
   ○ One bird are yellow.

4. ○ Those roses am red.
   ○ Those roses was red.
   ⊗ Those roses were red.

5. ⊗ I am next to the butterfly.
   ○ I are next to the butterfly.
   ○ I is next to the butterfly.

6. ○ We am happy in the trees.
   ⊗ We are happy in the trees.
   ○ We was happy in the trees.

Home Activity Your child prepared for taking tests on *am, is, are, was,* and *were.* Together read part of a newspaper or magazine article. Have your child circle the verbs *am, is, are, was,* and *were.*

Name _____

Circle the word for each picture.

small   small**er**   small**est**

1. (faster) fastest

2. bigger (biggest)

3. (taller) tallest

4. sweeter (sweetest)

5. (thicker) thickest

6. (thinner) thinnest

Write -er or -est to finish the word in each sentence.

7. The little bird has the few **est** eggs.

8. The little bird has a long **er** tail than the big bird.

 Home Activity Your child identified the comparative endings -er and -est as in *smaller* and *smallest*. Discuss the sizes, shapes, and colors of animals. Have your child compare the animals using -er when comparing two and -est when comparing more than two.

© Pearson Education, Inc., 1

Name _____

Read the words in the box.
Pick a word that is the opposite of each word below.
Write it on the line.

before   good-bye   right   won't

1. after

before

2. will

won't

3. hello

good-bye

$$\begin{array}{r} 2 \\ +2 \\ \hline 4 \end{array}$$

4. wrong

right

Pick a word from the box to finish each sentence.
Write it on the line. **Remember** to use capital letters.

oh   does

5. **Does** a bear start its long sleep in the spring?

6. **Oh** , no. It sleeps when the days start to get cold.

© Pearson Education, Inc., 1

School + Home **Home Activity** Your child identified and read the words *before, good-bye, right,* and *won't.* Write the opposite of these words on cards and mix them up. Have your child match the words that are opposites and then read the pairs. Then have him or her write two sentences using *does* and *oh.*

Name _____

Read the story.

Circle the answer to each question.

Zak has a puppy with the name Sparky.

Zak is sitting on his bed.

Sparky puts his nose under the bed.

I. Why do you think Sparky puts his nose under the bed?

Sparky wants to get up on the bed.

⟨Sparky wants something under the bed⟩

Zak finds a ball under the bed.

Sparky starts barking!

2. Why do you think Sparky starts barking?

⟨Sparky wants to play with the ball.⟩

Sparky wants Zak to pet him.

Then Zak starts to go outside.

Sparky jumps up and down!

3. Why do you think Sparky jumps up and down?

Sparky likes to jump up and down.

⟨Sparky wants to play outside with Zak.⟩

Home Activity Your child drew conclusions about a story. Reread the story with your child. Have your child tell you what he or she already knew about dogs that helped him or her draw conclusions.

Comprehension Draw Conclusions **395**

© Pearson Education, Inc., 1

Name _____

A Friendly Phone Call

Goose: Hello?

Raccoon: Hi, Goose! How are you?

Squirrel: We wish you were here!

Goose: I miss my friends. But I can't stand the cold.

Raccoon: It sure is cold here. We went ice skating.

Goose: I went fishing today.

Squirrel: When will you come home?

Goose: I will be back in spring.

Raccoon: We can't wait!

Squirrel: 'Bye, Goose.

Key Features of a Play Scene

• is written to be acted for an audience

• characters have lines to say

Name _____

Pick a word from the box to finish each sentence.
Write it on the line.

fudge   hedge   judge   ledge   smudge

ba**dge**

1. Mom made **fudge** for us to eat.

2. She set it on the **ledge** .

3. Did it fall into the **hedge** ?

4. Look, there's a **smudge** on Bear's face.

5. The **judge** thinks Bear ate it too.

Home Activity Your child learned to read words that end with *-dge* that have the sound heard in *judge*.
Have your child make a list of words that rhyme with *judge* (*budge, fudge, nudge, grudge, smudge, trudge*).

© Pearson Education, Inc., 1

Name _____

Words with -er, -est

Spelling Words				
bigger	biggest	faster	fastest	taller
tallest	shorter	shortest	sadder	saddest

Look at the pictures. **Write** list words that end with **-er** and **-est**.

short   1. **shorter**   2. **shortest**

fast   3. **faster**   4. **fastest**

big   5. **bigger**   6. **biggest**

Write a list word that rhymes with the underlined word.

7. This plant is <u>smaller</u> than that **taller** one.

8. The forest has the <u>smallest</u> and the **tallest** trees.

9. His face grew **sadder** as he put away the <u>ladder</u>.

10. This is the **saddest** and the <u>maddest</u> he's ever been.

School + Home   **Home Activity** Your child spelled words that end with -er and -est. Say a base word, such as *big*. Ask your child to say and spell the -er and -est words (*bigger, biggest*).

© Pearson Education, Inc., 1

Contractions with *Not*

A **contraction** is a short way to put two words together. A **verb** and the word **not** can be put together to make a contraction. An **apostrophe (')** is used in place of the letter **o** in **not**.

are + not = aren't   has + not = hasn't
did + not = didn't   is + not = isn't
do + not = don't   was + not = wasn't
does + not = doesn't   were + not = weren't

Circle the contraction in each sentence.

1. The animals (don't) have much time.

2. Caterpillar (doesn't) come out until spring.

3. Goose (isn't) staying for the winter.

Write the contraction for the underlined words.

4. The leaves <u>are not</u> on the trees.

aren't

5. Raccoon <u>was not</u> leaving the forest.

wasn't

School + Home **Home Activity** Your child learned about contractions with *not*. Read a story with your child. Have your child look for contractions with *not* and tell the two words that were put together to make each contraction.

Name _____

Idea Web

Squirrel: What have you been doing?

Goose: I went swimming.

Catching Up

Raccoon: We went ice skating.

Raccoon: Let's go fishing when I get home.

School + Home **Home Activity** Your child has ideas for a play scene. Have him or her explain how actors in a play perform a story.

Name _____

J

j

Copy the words. Write your letters the correct size.

Jack   Jack

Jill   Jill

Jake   Jake

jar   jar

just   just

jelly   jelly

judge   judge

jog   jog

jam   jam

Jon   Jon

wedge   wedge

lodge   lodge

jiffy   jiffy

Jane   Jane

Did you write your letters the correct size? | Yes | | No |

Home Activity Your child practiced writing words with *Jj* and *dge*. Have your child choose some words from the chart and use those words in a sentence.

Name _____

Luke asked his classmates what animals they like the most.
Help Luke complete the picture graph.

Favorite Pets

Number of Children: 5, 4, 3, 2, 1, 0

Cat   Dog   Fish   Hamster   Snake

I. Five classmates like cats the most. **Draw** five cats on the picture graph.

2. Five classmates like dogs the most. **Draw** five dogs on the picture graph.

3. Three classmates like fish the most. **Draw** three fish on the picture graph.

4. Four classmates like hamsters the most. **Draw** four hamsters on the picture graph.

5. Two classmates like snakes the most. **Draw** two snakes on the picture graph.

Home Activity Your child learned to read and complete a picture graph. Together, make a picture graph that shows information about your favorite animals and that of your friends and family.

The Contest

Comparative Endings -er and -est	Consonant Pattern -dge	High-Frequency Words	
bigger hardest	judge	have	the
harder darkest	edge	a	is
biggest sharpest	fudge	said	

"Let's have a contest," said Bart.

"Jess will be the judge."

Sit on the edge, Jess."

"My fudge is darkest," said Jess.

"My pencil is sharpest."

"You're not the judge anymore!" said Bart.

4

Decodable Story *The Contest*
Target Skill Comparative Endings -er and -est, Consonant Pattern -dge

"My plant is big," said Bart.

"My plant is bigger than that plant," said Sandy.

"Mine is the biggest," said Jess.

"See this hard trick?" said Bart.

"My trick is harder," said Sandy.

"My trick is the hardest yet," said Jess.

Name _____

Words with *-er, -est*

Spelling Words
bigger biggest faster fastest taller
tallest shorter shortest sadder saddest

High-Frequency Words
good-bye
before

Add *-er* or *-est*. **Write** the list word.

1. Tad is the tall___ boy in our class.

tallest

2. The fast___ runner will win the race.

fastest

3. My bat is short___ than yours.

shorter

4. I need some bigg___ shoes.

bigger

5. That is the sadd___ clown I've ever seen.

saddest

6. You walk fast___ than I do.

faster

7. The story made her feel even sadd___.

sadder

8. This is the world's bigg___ pizza.

biggest

Write a word that is the opposite of each word.

9. after **before**

10. hello **good-bye**

Home Activity Your child wrote spelling words to complete sentences. Help your child make up a new sentence for each spelling word.

Name _____

Contractions with *Not*

Write a sentence about each season.
Use a contraction with *not* in each sentence.

Winter **Possible answers:**

_____

Winter isn't hot.

Spring

_____

Days aren't cold in the spring.

Summer

_____

Summer doesn't last long.

Fall

_____

Trees don't stay green in the fall.

School + Home **Home Activity** Your child learned how to use contractions with *not* in writing. Write these sentences on paper: *He does not like winter. They do not like summer. She is not sad in the fall. We are not cold in the spring.* Have your child write the sentences using contractions with *not*.

Name _____

Words with -*er*, -*est*

Spelling Words				
bigger	biggest	faster	fastest	taller
tallest	shorter	shortest	sadder	saddest

Finish the list words.

1. **taller**

2. **shorter**

3. **tallest**

4. **shortest**

5. **sadder**

6. **biggest**

7. **bigger**

8. **saddest**

Write the missing words.

Froggy   Hopper

9. Hopper is **faster** than Froggy.

10. Hopper is **fastest** .

fastest
faster

Home Activity Your child has been learning to spell words ending in -*er* and -*est*. Play a game with your child by tossing a coin onto this page. Read the list word that is closest to where the coin lands and have your child spell it. Take turns.

Contractions with *Not*

Mark the sentence that spells the contraction correctly.

1. ⊗ Days aren't long in the winter.
   ○ Days arent long in the winter.
   ○ Days are'nt long in the winter.

2. ○ A raccoon does'nt sleep all winter long.
   ○ A raccoon doesnt sleep all winter long.
   ⊗ A raccoon doesn't sleep all winter long.

3. ○ The chrysalis hasnt moved at all.
   ⊗ The chrysalis hasn't moved at all.
   ○ The chrysalis has'nt moved at all.

4. ○ Bears do'nt come out until spring.
   ○ Bears dont come out until spring.
   ⊗ Bears don't come out until spring.

5. ⊗ Many birds didn't stay here.
   ○ Many birds did'nt stay here.
   ○ Many birds didnt stay here.

6. ○ The fat bear was'nt hungry.
   ⊗ The fat bear wasn't hungry.
   ○ The fat bear wasnt hungry.

© Pearson Education, Inc., 1

Home Activity Your child prepared for taking tests on contractions with *not*. Together read part of a short newspaper or magazine article. Take turns with your child circling contractions with *not*. Ask your child what two words make up each contraction.

t**ai**l →

pl**ay**

Circle the word for each picture.

1.	2.	3.	4.

(mail) mall   (tray) tree   pal (pail)   (pan) pain

5.	6.	7.	8.

sell (sail)   he (hay)   (train) trap   page (pay)

Find the word that has the same **long a** sound as ⋮⋮ .
Mark the ⬭ to show your answer.

9. ⬭ clip
    ⬭ clap
    ⬬ clay

10. ⬭ man
    ⬬ main
    ⬭ mine

Home Activity Your child read words in which the long a sound is spelled *ai* and *ay*, as in *rain* and *hay*. Ask your child to name a rhyming word for each long a word on this page.

Name _____

Read the words in the box.
Pick a word to complete each sentence.
Look at the scrambled letters for a hint.
Write the word on the line.

> about   enjoy   gives   surprise
> surprised   worry   would

1. I ___**enjoy**___ helping. **nyjeo**

2. We eat at ___**about**___ 12:00. **buato**

3. ___**Would**___ you please help me? **odluw**

4. Do not ___**worry**___ . I will help. **woryr**

5. When we jump up, she will be ___**surprised**___ . **sipresrud**

6. Dad ___**gives**___ us gifts. **ivseg**

7. The gifts are always a big ___**surprise**___ . **rrpsiues**

© Pearson Education, Inc., 1

Home Activity Your child identified and read the words *about, enjoy, gives, surprise, surprised, worry,* and *would*. Ask your child to use these words to create a puppet show with paper bag puppets. Record the script on paper and have your child practice reading it aloud.

Name _____

Look at the picture.
Circle the sentence that tells about the picture.

1.

Dad is happy about his new shed from Jen.

(Jen is happy about her tree house from Dad.)

2.

(They planted a garden.)

Flowers grow in gardens.

3.

We are singing in the play.

(The class sets up for a play.)

4.

(Tom is good at running.)

Tom is a good friend.

Write a sentence about the picture.

5.

Possible answers: Mom makes a cake.

Mom has a birthday surprise.

Home Activity Your child drew conclusions from pictures. Look at a story with your child. Cover up the words with paper. Invite your child to tell you about the story using only the illustrations.

Comprehension Draw Conclusions   **411**

Name _____

Dear Ken,

   It is almost your birthday!

What gift do you hope to get?

Do you want it to be a surprise?

Mom will take me to your party.

I will bring your gift then.

I hope you will like it.

Your friend,

Jill

Key Features of a Friendly Letter

- The letter is written to someone the writer knows.

- The letter has a polite greeting and closing.

Name _____

Write each word correctly.
Use 's or ' at the end of each word.

Meg**'s** hat

---

1. Janes drum = **Jane's** drum

2. dogs bone = **dog's** bone

3. Moms cup = **Mom's** cup

4. babys crib = **baby's** crib

5. pets beds = **pets'** beds

Pick a word from the box to match each picture.
Write it on the line.

girls'   Matt's

6. **Matt's** lunch

---

7. **girls'** games

Home Activity Your child wrote words that show ownership. Point out objects in your home that are owned by one or more persons in the family. Ask your child to use a possessive to tell you who owns each object (*Mike's pen*).

© Pearson Education, Inc., 1

Name _____

Words with *ai, ay*

Spelling Words				
train	way	tail	play	day
may	rain	gray	mail	afraid

Write the words in ABC order.

tail	afraid	way	may	gray	day

1. **afraid**

2. **day**

3. **gray**

4. **may**

5. **tail**

6. **way**

Draw a line from the word to its picture. **Write** the word.

mail

rain

train

play

7. **mail**

8. **rain**

9. **play**

10. **train**

Home Activity Your child spelled words with the long *a* sound spelled *ai* and *ay*. Have your child circle *ai* and *ay* in the spelling words.

Name _____

Adjectives

An **adjective** tells about a person, place, animal, or thing.

happy woman

big city

loud dog

nice present

Circle the adjective. **Write** the adjective on the line.
Say a sentence for each adjective.

1. (heavy) piñata   **heavy**

2. (bright) lights   **bright**

3. (hot) tortillas   **hot**

4. (good) friends   **good**

5. (sweet) rolls   **sweet**

School + Home   **Home Activity** Your child learned about adjectives. Read a story with your child. Point to a sentence and ask your child to identify any adjectives in the sentence. Continue with other sentences.

Name _____

Web

Home Activity Your child is learning more about writing a letter. Have your child plan a letter to a relative.

Name _____

M   m

Copy the words. Write the letters the correct size.

Meg	Meg	March	March
main	main	mail	mail
May	May	stay	stay
maid	maid	chain	chain
play	play	fail	fail
rain	rain	paid	paid
Max	Max	way	way

Did you write all of your letters the correct size? | **Yes** | | **No** |

Home Activity Your child practiced writing words with *Mm*, *ai*, and *ay*. Have your child read and copy the following sentence as neatly as he or she can. *Meg may stay and play in the rain.*

© Pearson Education, Inc., 1

Handwriting 417

Name _____

Find out about foods people make for celebrations.

chef

classmates

1. Who would you interview to find out foods that different families eat at celebrations?

   classmates

2. Who would you interview to find out how to make some of those foods?

   chef

3. Write a question to ask classmates about foods at their family celebrations.

   Possible question: What food do you always have at a family celebration?

4. Ask four classmates your question. Record their responses. Share the information with your class.

   Responses will vary.

Home Activity Your child learned about gathering information by interviewing people. Talk with your child about special traditions your family has for different celebrations. Ask you child to write two interview questions to ask a member of your family about the celebrations and traditions.

© Pearson Education, Inc., 1

Quails

Vowel Digraphs *ai, ay*		Singular and Plural Possessives	High-Frequency Words	
quails	stay	birds'	are	what
main	say	farmers'	their	do
trail	may	quail's	is	one
raid	someday		the	you
gray			many	a
			live	

Quails are small, plump birds.

Quails can fly, but their main home is on land.

What do quails say?

One quail's call is *bob . . . WHITE!*

You may see a bobwhite someday!

4

Decodable Story *Quails*
Target Skills Vowel Digraphs *ai, ay;* Singular and Plural Possessives

Many quails are tan, gray, and white.

The birds' spots and stripes help them hide.

They run up the trail when foxes raid.

2

Quails can live on farmers' farms.

They like seeds and insects.

Farmers hope the quails will stay!

3

Name _____

Words with *ai, ay*

Spelling Words				
train	way	tail	play	day
may	rain	gray	mail	afraid

High-Frequency Words
about
would

Read about a dog. **Write** the missing list words.

1. I have a __**gray**__ dog.

2. He is __**afraid**__ of storms.

3. He hides when it starts to __**rain**__ .

4. He barks when he hears a __**train**__ .

5. Could he learn a __**way**__ to play catch?

6. Could he fetch the __**mail**__ ?

7. I think he __**may**__ learn.

8. Look at him wag his __**tail**__ .

9. I think he __**would**__ like to play.

10. Let's think __**about**__ training another day.

Home Activity Your child wrote spelling words to complete a story about a dog. Have your child make up a story, using some of the list words.

Adjectives

Write an adjective from the box to complete each sentence.

> green   sharp   soft

1. Gina's cat has __soft__ fur.

2. The cat has __green__ eyes.

3. Look at the cat's __sharp__ claws.

Tell about something you like.
Use adjectives to describe it.

Possible answer: I love my

new ring. It has a blue stone.

It is a beautiful ring.

Choose other adjectives. Say a sentence for each adjective.

Home Activity Your child learned how to use adjectives in writing. Take turns with your child describing what you are wearing. Have your child identify any adjectives either of you uses in your descriptions.

© Pearson Education, Inc., 1

Name _____

Words with *ai, ay*

Spelling Words				
train	way	tail	play	day
may	rain	gray	mail	afraid

Underline the words that rhyme. **Write** the words.

Whose <u>tail</u> is on the <u>mail</u>?

1. **tail**

2. **mail**

Is there a <u>train</u> in the <u>rain</u>?

3. **train**

4. **rain**

When <u>may</u> we <u>play</u>?

5. **may**

6. **play**

Circle the word that is spelled correctly.

7. (gray)   gra

8. (day)   dai

9. afrayd   (afraid)

10. waye   (way)

Home Activity Your child has been learning to spell words with the long *a* sound spelled *ai* and *ay*. Help your child think of and spell words that rhyme with some of the list words.

Name _____

Adjectives

Mark the sentence that has a line under the adjective.

1. ⊗ Grandmother reads a <u>funny</u> book.
   ○ Grandmother <u>reads</u> a funny book.
   ○ <u>Grandmother</u> reads a funny book.

2. ○ Mama <u>gave</u> Francisco a big hug.
   ⊗ Mama gave Francisco a <u>big</u> hug.
   ○ Mama gave Francisco a big <u>hug</u>.

3. ○ Francisco <u>made</u> a colorful piñata.
   ○ Francisco <u>made</u> a colorful piñata.
   ⊗ Francisco made a <u>colorful</u> piñata.

4. ○ Everyone <u>ate</u> the fresh tortillas.
   ○ Everyone ate the fresh <u>tortillas</u>.
   ⊗ Everyone ate the <u>fresh</u> tortillas.

5. ○ The <u>party</u> was the best present.
   ⊗ The party was the <u>best</u> present.
   ○ The party was the best <u>present</u>.

6. ⊗ Papa played a <u>long</u> song.
   ○ Papa <u>played</u> a long song.
   ○ <u>Papa</u> played a long song.

Choose other adjectives. **Say** a sentence for each adjective.

Home Activity Your child prepared for taking tests on adjectives. Together read a short, simple newspaper or magazine article. Have your child circle as many adjectives as he or she can find.

Name _____

Circle the word for each picture.

1.

(head) herd

2.

bride (bead)

3.

sail (seal)

4.

berry (bread)

5.

(leaf) loaf

6.

(jeans) jars

7.

bake (beak)

8.

(clean) clang

Circle the words that finish each sentence.

9. (Please)/Place pass the (peas)/bees.

10. I (spread)/spent the jam on the cracker.

11. I (read)/rang my book at the (beach)/birch yesterday.

Home Activity Your child read words in which the long e sound is spelled *ea*. Ask your child to think of rhyming words for the words on this page. Write each word and review the vowel spelling together.

Phonics Vowel Digraph *ea* **425**

Name _____

Read the words in the box.
Pick a word to complete each sentence.
Write the word on the line.

> draw   colors   over
> drew   great   sign   show

1. Each day I like to _____**draw**_____ in art class.

2. Ted did a _____**great**_____ job on his drawing!

3. I can read the _____**sign**_____ on the gate.

4. I think red and blue are the best _____**colors**_____ .

5. The map will _____**show**_____ us the way to go.

6. The frogs jump _____**over**_____ the rocks.

7. Last week I _____**drew**_____ a dog in art class.

Home Activity Your child identified and read the words *draw, colors, over, drew, great, sign,* and *show.* Have your child read each word again and make up a new sentence for each word.

© Pearson Education, Inc., 1

Read the story.
Follow the directions.

One day, Penny and her mom went to East Mall. Mom wanted to get jeans for Penny. East Mall was a big mall. Penny and her mom spent a long time walking from store to store. Soon Penny wanted to go home. But her mom wanted to go to one more store. At last, they got jeans for Penny. Then they headed home. Penny went into the house first. She saw paper chains everywhere! She saw a cake. Then her friends came running and yelled, "Surprise, Penny!"

I. Circle the sentence that is the big idea of the story.

Penny and her mom walked around a big mall.

(Penny's friends gave her a surprise birthday party.)

2. Circle why you think Mom spent a long time at the mall.

(She wanted Penny's friends to get to the house before Penny)

On that day, she wanted to spend a lot of time with Penny.

3. Write a title for this story

Possible titles: A Party for Penny; A Surprise for

Penny; Happy Birthday, Penny

Home Activity Your child identified the theme—the big idea—of a story. Reread the story with your child. Help your child identify the sentences in the story that helped him or her tell the big idea.

Name _____

Dear Emma,

My older brother plays soccer. He will give a free soccer lesson to kids. Please come to the lesson. It will be at my house on April 20 at 3:00 p.m. I hope you will come.

Your friend,
Kat

Key Features of an Invitation

• An invitation asks someone to an event, using polite words.

• An invitation tells important information about the event.

© Pearson Education, Inc., 1

Name _____

Add -ed to each word.
Write the new word on the line.

fr**ied**

1. dry

dried

2. cry

cried

3. spy

spied

4. worry

worried

5. try

tried

6. copy

copied

Add -er and **-est** to each word.
Write the new word on the lines.

	Add -er	Add -est
7. silly	**sillier**	**silliest**
8. funny	**funnier**	**funniest**
9. happy	**happier**	**happiest**
10. easy	**easier**	**easiest**

Home Activity Your child practiced adding endings to words where the spelling changed from *y* to *i* before adding *-ed, -er,* or *-est*. Use the words above to make up a story with your child.

Name _____

Cinderella

Words with *ea*.

Spelling Words

eat	sea	each	team	please
dream	treat	beach	clean	lean

Write two list words that rhyme with the picture.

1. **each**
2. **beach**
3. **clean**
4. **lean**
5. **eat**
6. **treat**

Write the missing words.

Spelling Words

sea	please
team	dream

7. My **team** won!

8. I **dream** about trips.

9. I love the **sea**.

10. Can we **please** go there?

Home Activity Your child spelled words with the long e sound spelled *ea*. Ask your child to name the two letters that appear in every spelling word (*ea*).

430 **Spelling** Words with *ea*

Name _____

Adjectives for Colors and Shapes

Some **adjectives** name colors.

white crayon **black** pencil

Some **adjectives** name shapes.

square paper **round** frame

Circle the adjective in each sentence that names a color or shape.
Say a sentence for each adjective.

1. Roz has (blue) markers.

2. Gert has (green) markers.

3. Roz draws (round) circles.

4. Gert draws (square) boxes.

5. Roz adds (brown) dots.

6. Gert makes (yellow) lines.

School + Home **Home Activity** Your child learned about adjectives for colors and shapes. Point to objects around your home and have your child describe the objects using adjectives that name colors and shapes.

Name _____

Web

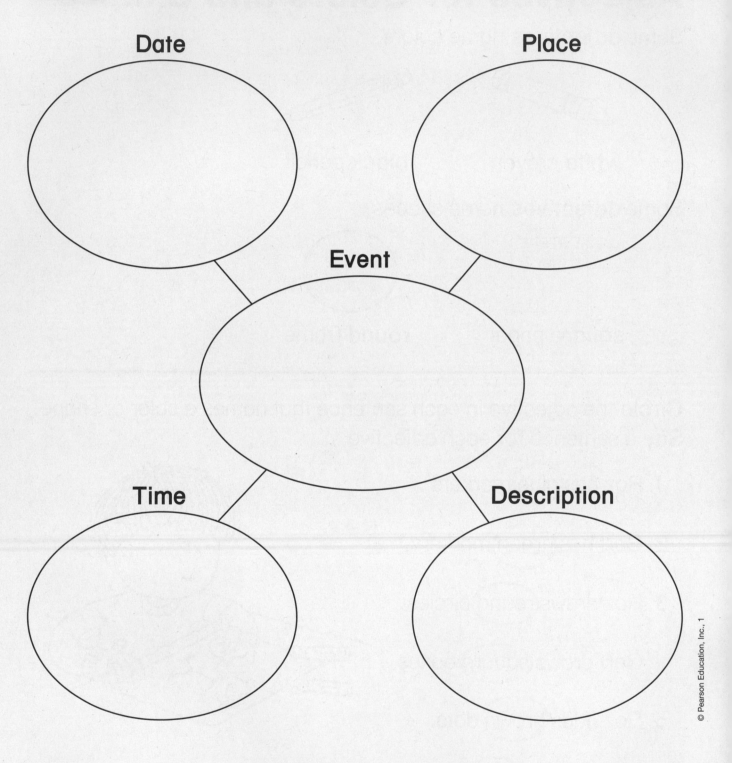

Date

Place

Event

Time

Description

School + Home

Home Activity Your child is learning about invitations. Share ideas about how people invite family members to events.

Name _____

L   l

Copy the words. Leave the correct space between your letters.

Len	Len	bead	bead
lean	lean	Leah	Leah
leap	leap	leaf	leaf
plea	plea	sea	sea
seal	seal	beam	beam
clean	clean	seat	seat
leak	leak	heap	heap

Did you leave the correct space between your letters? Yes   No

© Pearson Education, Inc., 1

Home Activity Your child practiced writing words with *Ll* and *ea*. Have your child choose one word with *ea* and write as many rhyming words as he or she can from words on the list and not on the list.

Name _____

Jordan asked her classmates which story is their favorite.
Help Jordan complete the chart.

Favorite Stories	
Goldilocks	卌
The Three Little Pigs	IIII
Little Red Riding Hood	III
The Tortoise and the Hare	II
The Billy Goats Gruff	卌 I

卌 = 5

Make tally marks on the chart to show what Jordan learned.

I. Five classmates like **Goldilocks** the most.

2. Four classmates like **The Three Little Pigs** the most.

3. Three classmates like **Little Red Riding Hood** the most.

4. Two classmates like **The Tortoise and the Hare** the most.

5. Six classmates like **The Three Billy Goats Gruff** the most.

6. Present Jordan's results to your class by acting out the story
that her classmates liked the most.
Children should act out Three Billy Goats Gruff.

Home Activity Your child used a chart to find information, answer questions, and convey results of
research. Together, make a chart showing chores that each family member does at home. Ask your child to
fill in the chart as chores are completed.

Name _____

Bread

Vowel Digraph *ea*		Adding Endings: Change *y* to *i*	High-Frequency Words	
bread	yeast	babies	a	I
eat	treat	ladies	your	the
feast	leave	dried	are	is
wheat	meal	fried	you	you
read	clean	tried	about	
beat			said	

"Babies like it! Ladies like it!

Eat it with jelly!

It's a feast in your belly!" sang Neal.

"This is a treat!" said Beth.

"But I must leave after the meal."

"No . . . after we clean up!" said Neal.

Decodable Story *Bread*
Target Skills Vowel Digraph *ea*; Adding Endings: Changing *y* to *i*

"Are you singing about bread?"
asked Beth.

"Yes!" said Neal. "I'm mixing
wheat bread.

"Will you help me?"

"I've never tried that before,"
said Beth.

"But I can read the card.

I'll beat in the yeast."

Name _____

Words with *ea*

Spelling Words				
eat	sea	each	team	please
dream	treat	beach	clean	lean

High-Frequency Words
colors
sign

Write the missing letters. **Write** the word.

1. Is it time to **eat** ?   **eat**

2. Let's go to the **b eac h** .   **beach**

3. I can **c l ean** the porch.   **clean**

4. Don't **l ean** over too far.   **lean**

5. I had a **d r eam** last night.   **dream**

6. Will you **p l eas e** sit?   **please**

7. Fish live in the **s ea** .   **sea**

8. My **t eam** lost!   **team**

Write a word that rhymes with each word.

9. favors **colors**   10. fine **sign**

Home Activity Your child wrote spelling words to complete sentences. Read a sentence on this page and have your child spell the list word.

© Pearson Education, Inc., 1

Adjectives for Colors and Shapes

Color the boxes and circles.

Write about the picture.
Use color and shape words.
Possible answer:

The picture has square boxes. It has round circles. There are blue boxes and green boxes. There are red circles and yellow circles.

Choose other adjectives. **Say** a sentence for each adjective.

Home Activity Your child learned how to use adjectives for colors and shapes in writing. Write this sentence frame on paper: *The ___ animal runs.* Have your child write color adjectives in the sentence frame to make as many sentences as possible.

© Pearson Education, Inc., 1

Name _____

Words with *ea*

Write list words in the puzzle.

Across
2. chew food
4. not dirty

Down
1. sandy shore
3. ocean
5. thin

Spelling Words

Spelling Words:
eat
sea
each
team
please
dream
treat
beach
clean
lean

Crossword puzzle:
1. b
   e
   a
4. c l e a n
   h
3. s
   e
   a
5. l
2. e a t
   a
   n

Draw lines through all the *i*'s and *k*'s. **Write** the word that is left.

6. t i̶ e k̶ a k̶ m i̶   **team**

7. p l i̶ e a k̶ k̶ s i̶ e   **please**

8. k̶ t i̶ r e k̶ a k̶ i̶ t   **treat**

9. e i̶ a k̶ c i̶ k̶ h   **each**

10. d i̶ r k̶ i̶ e a m   **dream**

Home Activity Your child has been learning to spell words with the long *e* sound spelled *ea*. Have your child identify and spell the three words he or she found most difficult.

© Pearson Education, Inc., 1

Adjectives for Colors and Shapes

Mark the sentence that has a line under the adjective.

1. ○ Will Cindy <u>draw</u> yellow flowers?
   ⊗ Will Cindy draw <u>yellow</u> flowers?
   ○ Will Cindy draw yellow <u>flowers</u>?

2. ⊗ She makes <u>round</u> shapes.
   ○ She <u>makes</u> round shapes.
   ○ <u>She</u> makes round shapes.

3. ○ She adds green <u>stems</u>.
   ○ She <u>adds</u> green stems.
   ⊗ She adds <u>green</u> stems.

4. ⊗ Cindy cuts <u>brown</u> paper.
   ○ Cindy <u>cuts</u> brown paper.
   ○ <u>Cindy</u> cuts brown paper.

5. ○ She pastes it on square <u>boxes</u>.
   ⊗ She pastes it on <u>square</u> boxes.
   ○ She <u>pastes</u> it on square boxes.

6. ○ She makes lines <u>with</u> black markers.
   ○ She makes <u>lines</u> with black markers.
   ⊗ She makes lines with <u>black</u> markers.

Say a sentence for each adjective. **Choose** other adjectives.

Home Activity Your child prepared for taking tests on adjectives for colors and shapes. Together read a favorite book. Have your child point out adjectives that name colors and shapes.

Name _____

Circle the word for each picture.

 to<u>a</u>d   bl<u>ow</u>

1.	2.	3.	4.
snap (snow)	(road) rod	(boat) beat	sap (soap)

5.	6.	7.	8.
bee (bow)	(coat) cot	ray (row)	(leaf) loaf

Write the letters that finish the words in each sentence.

9. The g **oa** t drank from the b **ow** l.

10. They looked high and l **ow** but they could not find the

r **oa** d.

School + Home

Home Activity Your child created and read words in which the long o sound is spelled *oa* and *ow*, as in *toad* and *blow*. Together, list as many words as possible with the long o sound in their names. Then ask your child to sort the words by their spellings.

© Pearson Education, Inc., 1

Name _____

Read the words in the box.
Pick a word to finish each sentence.
Write it in the puzzle.

found   mouth   once   took   wild

1. You talk with your _____ .

2. "_____ upon a time . . ."

3. not lost

4. He _____ three bites
of his cake.

5. A raccoon is a _____ animal.

Puzzle:

1. m 2. o u t h
n
c
e

3. f
4. t o o k
u
n
5. w i l d

School + Home

Home Activity Your child identified and read the words *found, mouth, once, took,* and *wild*. Ask your child to write and illustrate a fairy tale about a boy or girl who finds a wild animal. Encourage your child to use the new words and help him or her with spelling if necessary.

Name _____

Read the details.
Circle the details that are from the story you just read.

1. (The President is the leader of our country.)

   There are three fish in the pond.

   (The U.S. Constitution is a plan for our government.)

   My father made me a tree house.

   (Laws are rules that we follow.)

Write two facts about the story.

_____

2. Possible answers: The White House is in Washington, D.C.

   _____

   George Washington was our first President.

   _____

   The Potomac is a river in Washington, D.C.

   _____

   Accept all reasonable answers.

Home Activity Your child has learned to identify facts and details from a story. Read a story with your child and point out facts and details.

Name _____

 The Farm

We hop on the big yellow school bus.

To the farm it takes us.

Cows, pigs, and sheep we see!

But the best part of all

is watching the farmer haul

huge bales of hay

to the barn where the animals stay.

Key Features of a Descriptive Poem

· Most descriptive poems are shorter than a story.

· Lines in a descriptive poem can either rhyme or not rhyme.

Name _____

Circle the word for each picture.

1.

stub
(scrub)

2.

(splash)
slash

3.

(squeeze)
sneeze

4.

sting
(string)

5.

lint
(splint)

6.

(spring)
sing

7.

those
(three)

8.

(stripe)
ripe

Write the letters that finish the words in each sentence.

9. She _____ **thr** _____ e w the ball _____ **thr** _____ o u g h the

_____ **scr** _____ e e n door.

10. I had a sore _____ **thr** _____ o a t .

© Pearson Education, Inc., 1

Home Activity Your child created and read words that begin with three-letter consonant blends. Have your child draw pictures of *screen, spray, squint,* and *street.* Have him or her label each picture with the word.

Name _____

Words with *oa, ow*

Read the clues. **Write** the word.

Spelling Words

boat
road
snow
row
yellow
loaf
coat
soap
blow
pillow

It rhymes with **willow**.
You sleep on it.

1. __pillow__

It rhymes with **goat**.
It goes in water.

2. __boat__

It rhymes with **mow**.
It's cold and white.

3. __snow__

It rhymes with **fellow**.
It's a color.

4. __yellow__

It rhymes with **load**.
Cars go on it.

5. __road__

It rhymes with **goat**.
You wear it.

6. __coat__

Write the missing word.

7. I like to ____ bubbles.

8. Did you ____ the boat?

9. I got ____ in my eyes.

10. The ____ of bread is warm.

__blow__

__row__

__soap__

__loaf__

Home Activity Your child spelled words with the long *o* vowel sound spelled *oa* and *ow*. Have your child underline *oa* and *ow* in the spelling words.

Adjectives for Sizes

Some **adjectives** describe size. Words such as **big, small, long,** and **short** describe size.

small bird

big bird

Circle each adjective that describes size.
Say a sentence for each adjective.

1. (big) bus

2. (long) river

3. (little) fish

4. (short) stripes

5. (tall) window

6. (huge) flag

School +Home

Home Activity Your child learned about adjectives for sizes. Point to objects around your home. Ask your child if the object is big or small (tall or short, long or short). Have your child answer using the adjective in a sentence.

Name _____

A Place and What You See

Home Activity Your child can plan a poem that describes a place. Look at pictures of a place with your child. Describe it.

Name _____

F   f

Copy the words. Write the letters from left to right.

Flo   Flo   Fred   Fred

float   float   goat   goat

boat   boat   grow   grow

flow   flow   foam   foam

loaf   loaf   throat   throat

road   road   blow   blow

moan   moan   slow   slow

Did you write all of your letters from left to right? | Yes | | No |

© Pearson Education, Inc., 1

Home Activity Your child practiced writing words with *Ff* and *oa*. Have your child read and write any five words with the letter *F* or *v* from the list one more time.

Name _____

Ray asked his friends about their favorite American treasures.
Help Ray complete the bar graph.

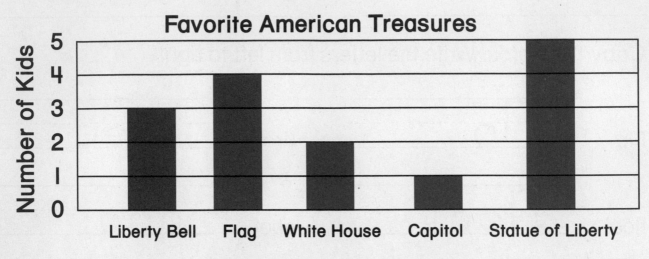

Favorite American Treasures

Make bars on the graph to show what Ray learned.

1. Three friends like the Liberty Bell the most.

2. Four friends like the American Flag the most.

3. Two friends like the White House the most.

4. One friend likes the Capitol the most.

5. Five friends like the Statue of Liberty the most.

6. Present Ray's results to your class by dramatizing the American treasure that his friends liked the most.

Children should dramatize the Statue of Liberty.

Home Activity Your child learned how to make and read a bar graph. Help your child poll family members and friends about their favorite places to visit. Make a bar graph to record the results.

Name _____

It's Spring!

Vowel Digraphs oa, ow			3-Letter Consonant Blends, Including thr, spl		High-Frequency Words	
toad	snow	show	spring	thrill	the	a
croaks	crow	throw	splash	street	what	your
boat	flowers	yellow	sprout		do	out
goat	row		stream		you	is
oats	grow		stretch		to	

The snow went away. It's spring!

The crow flies. The toad croaks.

The fish splash. The flowers sprout.

© Pearson Education, Inc., 1

Spring is a thrill!

Spring is the best season on my street . . . until summer, that is!

4

Decodable Story It's Spring!
Target Skills Vowel Digraphs oa, ow; 3-Letter Consonant Blends, Including thr, spl

What do you like to do in spring?

You can row a boat up the stream.

You can grow a rose.

2

You can throw a ball to a pal.

You can feed oats to the goat.

You can stretch out on the grass.

3

Name _____

Words with *oa, ow*

Spelling Words				
boat	road	snow	row	yellow
loaf	coat	soap	blow	pillow

High-Frequency Words
wild
once

Write the missing list word.

1. Lemons are __yellow__ .

2. Wash with __soap__ .

3. Would you like to ride in our __boat__ ?

4. I sleep on a soft __pillow__ .

5. Wear your __coat__ .

6. He will __row__ the boat.

7. Please buy a __loaf__ of bread.

8. Is it cold enough to __snow__ ?

9. I took this road __once__ .

10. The monkey is a __wild__ animal.

Home Activity Your child wrote spelling words to complete sentences. Ask your child to create a sentence using one or two of the spelling words.

Adjectives for Sizes

Write about something you like that is very big.
It might be an animal, a place, or a thing.
Use adjectives to tell about it.

Possible answer: I like our capital. It is a great city. The buildings are big.

Write about something you like that is very small.
It might be an animal, a place, or a thing.
Use adjectives to tell about it. **Say** the adjectives you used.

Possible answer: I like the stars on the flag. It has little stars. It has white stars.

School + Home **Home Activity** Your child learned how to use adjectives for sizes in writing. Point to pictures that show big, small, long, short, and tall things, one at a time. Ask: *What size is the ___?* Have your child answer the question.

Words with *oa, ow*

Spelling Words				
boat	road	snow	row	yellow
loaf	coat	soap	blow	pillow

Write the list word that belongs in the group.

blanket   sheet

1. **pillow**

blue   red

3. **yellow**

jacket   sweater

5. **coat**

rain   sleet

2. **snow**

street   highway

4. **road**

ship   ocean liner

6. **boat**

Circle the word that matches. **Write** it.

7. row   bow   (row) → **row**

8. loaf   load   (loaf) → **loaf**

9. blow   (blow) flow → **blow**

10. soap   soak   (soap) → **soap**

Home Activity Your child has been learning words with the long *o* vowel sound spelled *oa* and *ow*. Give clues about a word. Can your child guess and spell the word?

Adjectives for Sizes

Mark the sentence that has a line under the adjective.

1. ○ We <u>saw</u> a big bus.
   ○ We saw a big <u>bus</u>.
   ⊗ We saw a <u>big</u> bus.

2. ⊗ Look at the <u>huge</u> house.
   ○ <u>Look</u> at the huge house.
   ○ Look at the huge <u>house</u>.

3. ○ A long river <u>flows</u> by the road.
   ⊗ A <u>long</u> river flows by the road.
   ○ A long <u>river</u> flows by the road.

4. ○ The bird <u>has</u> a small fish.
   ○ The <u>bird</u> has a small fish.
   ⊗ The bird has a <u>small</u> fish.

5. ⊗ The fish has a <u>short</u> tail.
   ○ The fish <u>has</u> a short tail.
   ○ The fish has a short <u>tail</u>.

6. ○ A little bird was in the <u>sky</u>.
   ⊗ A <u>little</u> bird was in the sky.
   ○ A little bird <u>was</u> in the sky.

Choose other adjectives. **Say** a sentence for each adjective.

Home Activity Your child prepared for taking tests on adjectives for sizes. Together read a favorite storybook. Have your child find adjectives for sizes.

© Pearson Education, Inc., 1

Name _____

Circle the word for each picture.

1.	2.	3.	4.
(night) note	sit (lie)	(tie) tea	fit (fight)

5.	6.	7.	8.
pit (pie)	hay (high)	(sit) sight	(tight) toad

Read the sentences.
Circle the words that have the **long i** sound spelled **ie** and **igh**.
Underline the words that have the **long e** sound spelled **ie**.

9. I would like another <u>piece</u> of birthday cake.

10. He <u>believes</u> that he is (right).

11. I am sorry that I (lied) to you.

Home Activity Your child practiced reading words in which the long *i* sound is spelled *igh* and *ie* as in *light* and *pie*, and words in which the long *e* sound is spelled *ie*. Encourage your child to create a poem, nonsense rhyme, or song using *igh* and *ie* words.

Name _____

Read the words in the box.
Pick a word to match each clue.
Write it on the line.

> above   eight   laugh   moon   touch

1. "Ha, ha, ha!" __laugh__

2. eight (8) five, six, seven, __eight__

3. not below __above__

4. feel __touch__

5. stars, planets, __moon__

School + Home **Home Activity** Your child identified and read the words *above, eight, laugh, moon,* and *touch*. Act out clues for each word and have your child guess which word you picked.

Name _____

Read the story.

Nina and Anna are best friends. On Sunday, they will go to camp for one week. They will sleep in a tent. They will meet other girls. They will go swimming. At night they can watch the moon and the stars. Nina and Anna will have a good time.

Read the details. **Circle** the details that are from the story.

⟨They will sleep in tents.⟩

⟨They will go swimming.⟩

They will look for shells.

Camp is a long way from their home.

⟨At night they will watch the moon and the stars.⟩

Write two facts about the story.

_____

Possible answers: On Sunday, they will go to camp for one week.

_____

Nina and Anna are best friends.

_____

They will go to sleep.

_____

_____

Home Activity Your child has learned to identify facts and details from a story. Read a story with your child and ask your child to name one detail and one fact from the story.

© Pearson Education, Inc., 1

Name _____

Writing Prompt: Write a story about a child who rides a horse.

 Riley's Ride

Riley went with her family to the fair. There were horses there. Could she ride one? Riley's mom paid for a ride. Riley got to ride a horse. She picked a black and white horse. They went in circles around the field. It was fun!

Name _____

Circle the word for each picture.

__kn__ight   __wr__ench

1.	2.	3.	4.
(knife) night	rest (wrist)	(nine) knit	(knob) not

5.	6.	7.	8.
note (knot)	(wreck) rack	white (write)	(ring) wrong

Find the word that has the same beginning sound as the picture.
Mark the ⬭ to show your answer.

9. ⬛ wren
   ⬭ when
   ⬭ went

10. ⬭ sneak
   ⬭ kite
   ⬛ knock

Home Activity Your child read words that begin with *kn* as in *knight* and *wr* as in *wrench*. Have your child copy all the words from the page that begin with *kn* and *wr* and ask him or her to circle the silent letter in each word.

Name _____

Words with *ie, igh*

Spelling Words				
lie	tie	high	might	right
night	bright	light	pie	tight

Write the list word that names the picture.

1. __tie__   2. __pie__   3. __light__

Write the list word that means the same as the underlined word.

4. These gloves are too <u>snug</u>.

4. __tight__

5. What is the <u>correct</u> answer?

5. __right__

6. The wall is <u>tall</u>.

6. __high__

7. We pulled with all our <u>strength</u>.

7. __might__

8. Let's wait until <u>evening</u>.

8. __night__

9. She is very <u>smart</u>.

9. __bright__

10. I would not tell a <u>fib</u>.

10. __lie__

School + Home

Home Activity Your child spelled words with the long *i* sound spelled *ie* and *igh*. Have your child circle *ie* and *igh* in the spelling words.

Name _____

Adjectives for What Kind

An **adjective** can tell what kind.

warm day

pretty flowers

Write the adjective that tells what kind.
Say a sentence for each adjective.

1. loud cattle   **loud**

2. happy cows   **happy**

3. hot sun   **hot**

4. bright lights   **bright**

5. tall tree   **tall**

6. dark skies   **dark**

© Pearson Education, Inc., 1

Home Activity Your child learned about adjectives for what kind. Write *hot, cold, dry* in one list and the nouns *snow, sun, socks* in another list. Ask your child to combine the adjectives and nouns (*hot sun, cold snow, dry socks*).

Name _____

Realistic Story
Top Score Response

Focus/Ideas	A good realistic story clearly tells what characters do.
Organization	A good realistic story has a beginning, middle, and end.
Voice	A good realistic story shows the writer's and characters' feelings.
Word Choice	A good realistic story uses words that describe characters, setting, and events.
Sentences	A good realistic story has different kinds of sentences that are clear and complete.
Conventions	A good realistic story uses adjectives that tell what kind.

© Pearson Education, Inc., 1

Home Activity Your child is writing a story about children at a ranch. Share ideas about ranches in stories, movies, or experience.

Name _____

Z   z

Copy the words. Write your letters the correct size.

Zeke   Zeke   high   high

buzz   buzz   fizz   fizz

tie   tie   fried   fried

sigh   sigh   fuzz   fuzz

cried   cried   lie   lie

flies   flies   Zena   Zena

sight   sight   light   light

Did you write all of your letters the correct size?   Yes   No

School + Home

Home Activity Your child practiced writing words with *Zz*, *ie*, and *igh*. Have your child find three words from the list that rhyme with *sigh* and write them one more time. *(high, tie, lie)*

© Pearson Education, Inc., 1

Handwriting 465

Name _____

Read the guide words.
Write the word from the box that
you would find on that page.

┌─────────────────────────────────┐
│   tag bed hand hot cat   │
└─────────────────────────────────┘

1. hat   hunt
   _____
   ----- **hot** -----

2. bag   box
   _____
   ----- **bed** -----

3. book   cut
   _____
   ----- **cat** -----

4. sack   tend
   _____
   ----- **tag** -----

┌─────────────────────────────────┐
│   dog feed gone lip mint   │
└─────────────────────────────────┘

5. let   lock
   _____
   ----- **lip** -----

6. day   duck
   _____
   ----- **dog** -----

7. gas   gust
   _____
   ----- **gone** -----

8. man   mole
   _____
   ----- **mint** -----

© Pearson Education, Inc., 1

Home Activity Your child learned about using alphabetical order and guide words in a dictionary. Look through a children's dictionary with your child. Make a game of finding new words by using the guide words at the top of each page.

Name _____

The Gift

Vowel Digraphs *ie, igh*		Consonant Patterns *kn, wr*		High-Frequency Words	
brief	might	knee	wrench	a	were
chief	right	kneeled	wrapped	the	is
necktie	bright	knot		was	what
ties	tight	know		to	do
tie	sighed	wrong		said	too
night					

Carl went on a brief shopping trip.

The chief reason was to get a gift.

His dad's birthday party was that night.

1

Carl didn't know what to do.

Then he got a wrench instead.

He wrapped it. Dad liked it!

4

Decodable Story *The Gift*
Target Skills Vowel Digraphs *ie, igh*; Consonant Patterns *kn, wr*

"Dad might like a necktie," said Carl.

The ties were right by his knee.

Carl kneeled to see.

2

Carl tried on a bright red tie.

He made the knot too tight.

"This is all wrong!" he sighed.

3

Name _____

Words with *ie, igh*

Spelling Words				
lie	tie	high	might	right
night	bright	light	pie	tight

High-Frequency Words
above
laugh

Write a list word to finish the sentence.

1. You are r_____.

2. Turn on the l_____.

3. I love to eat p_____!

4. Will you wear a t_____?

5. The roof is h_____.

6. It's a cold n_____.

7. The stars are b_____.

8. My belt is too t_____.

9. Do not l_____ at us.

10. The sign is a_____ the school.

1. **right**

2. **light**

3. **pie**

4. **tie**

5. **high**

6. **night**

7. **bright**

8. **tight**

9. **laugh**

10. **above**

School + Home **Home Activity** Your child wrote spelling words to complete sentences. Help your child use the list words in new sentences.

© Pearson Education, Inc., 1

Adjectives for What Kind

Write about something your family does
on a holiday.
Use adjectives such as *loud*, *tasty*,
or *cold* to tell about it.

Possible answer: We have a great picnic on the Fourth of July. It is always a hot day. We make cold ice cream. We swim in the cool lake.

Choose other adjectives. **Say** a sentence for each adjective.

© Pearson Education, Inc., 1

Home Activity Your child learned how to use adjectives for what kind in writing. With sour child, look through a family photo album. Talk about what you see in photos using adjectives that tell what kind.

Name _____

Words with *ie, igh*

Draw a line through three rhyming list words in a row. **Write** the words.

might	read	lie
row	tie	tight
pie	loaf	road

pie	right	coat
sled	tight	low
blue	might	high

1. **lie**
2. **tie**
3. **pie**
4. **right**
5. **tight**
6. **might**

Write the missing words.

night   bright
light   high

7. It is up **high** .
8. It looks **bright** .
9. You see it at **night** .
10. It looks like a **light** .

Home Activity Your child has been learning to spell words with the long *i* sound spelled *ie* and *igh*. Say a list word. Ask your child how the long *i* sound is spelled (*ie* or *igh*).

© Pearson Education, Inc., 1

Adjectives for What Kind

Mark the sentence that has a line under the adjective.

1. ○ <u>Dinner</u> on Sunday is a great meal.
   ○ Dinner on <u>Sunday</u> is a great meal.
   ⊗ Dinner on Sunday is a <u>great</u> meal.

2. ⊗ A ranch hand bakes <u>fresh</u> bread.
   ○ A ranch hand <u>bakes</u> fresh bread.
   ○ A ranch hand bakes fresh <u>bread.</u>

3. ○ Another ranch hand makes spicy <u>stew.</u>
   ⊗ Another ranch hand makes <u>spicy</u> stew.
   ○ Another ranch hand <u>makes</u> spicy stew.

4. ⊗ I pour glasses of <u>cold</u> milk.
   ○ I <u>pour</u> glasses of cold milk.
   ○ I pour <u>glasses</u> of cold milk.

5. ○ Sweet oranges <u>are</u> our dessert.
   ⊗ <u>Sweet</u> oranges are our dessert.
   ○ Sweet <u>oranges</u> are our dessert.

6. ○ <u>We</u> wash the dirty dishes together.
   ○ We <u>wash</u> the dirty dishes together.
   ⊗ We wash the <u>dirty</u> dishes together.

Choose other adjectives. **Say** a sentence for each adjective.

Home Activity Your child prepared for taking tests on adjectives for what kind. Together read a short, simple newspaper or magazine article. Have your child circle adjectives that tell what kind.

© Pearson Education, Inc., 1

Name _____

Pick a word from the box to finish each compound word.
Write it on the line.
Draw a line to the picture it matches.

flashlight

boat   man   paper   watch

1. news **paper**

2. row **boat**

3. wrist **watch**

4. snow **man**

Find the compound word.

Mark the ⬭ to show your answer.

5. ⬭ raining
   ⬭ rainy
   ⬬ raincoat

6. ⬬ popcorn
   ⬭ puppy
   ⬭ popping

7. ⬭ mitten
   ⬭ marching
   ⬬ backpack

8. ⬭ balloon
   ⬬ daydream
   ⬭ broken

School + Home **Home Activity** Your child read compound words—words formed by joining two or more words. Have your child tell what two words make up these compound words: *rainbow, snowflake, peanut, baseball, backpack.*

Name _____

Read the words in the box.
Pick a word to finish each sentence.
Write it on the line.

picture   remember   room   stood   thought   would

1. Mom took a _____ **picture** _____ of my friends and me.

2. We _____ **stood** _____ by a tree.

3. I _____ **thought** _____ the picture was wonderful.

4. I will hang the picture in my _____ **room** _____ .

5. It will help me **remember** my friends.

Home Activity Your child learned to identify and read the words *picture, remember, room, stood,* and *thought.* Write each word on a small piece of paper. Say each word. Have your child put the words in the order in which you read them and then repeat the words in a different order.

Name _____

Read the story.
Underline the answer to each question.

Popcorn is a very old food. People in many
lands planted popcorn. They found out something
about this corn. Heat would make it pop! Other
corns would not pop. The popped corn looked
like snowflakes. Some people wore strings of
it around their neck or on their head. These people also ate the
popped corn. Other people ate popcorn in a bowl with milk.

1. What is the story all about?

   <u>popcorn</u>   snowflakes

2. What is the big idea of the story?

   <u>Long ago, people found many uses for popcorn.</u>

   People can wear strings of popped popcorn.

3. Why do you think some people wore strings of popcorn?

   They liked the color of the popped corn.

   <u>They liked the snowflake shape of the popped corn.</u>

© Pearson Education, Inc., 1

School + Home **Home Activity** Your child identified the theme—the big idea—of a story. Reread the story with your child.
Have your child underline the sentences in the story that helped him or her tell the big idea.

Name _____

Dear Hunter,

Thank you for sharing your basketball with me.
I had fun playing two games with you.

Your friend,
Cody

Key Features of a Thank-You Note

• A thank-you note thanks someone for doing something nice.

• It tells how the writer feels.

© Pearson Education, Inc., 1

School + Home

Home Activity Your child is learning about writing a thank-you note. Discuss ways of expressing thanks.

476   Writing Thank-You Note

Name _____

Circle the word for each picture.

1. (blew) black	2. flow (flew)	3. (glue) glow	4. chick (chew)
5. sit (suit)	6. (stew) stop	7. joke (juice)	8. (news) nose

Read the words in the box.
Pick a word to finish each sentence.

    bruise   drew   true

9. It is __**true**__ that I love ice cream.

10. He has a __**bruise**__ on his leg.

11. My sister __**drew**__ this picture.

 School + Home **Home Activity** Your child practiced reading words with *ew, ue,* and *ui* as in *grew, Sue,* and *fruit*. Work with your child to make up silly rhyming pairs that contain this vowel sound and these spellings, such as *blue stew* or *fruit suit*.

Phonics Vowel Digraphs *ew, ue, ui*   **477**

Name _____

Compound Words

Write the list word that names the picture.

1. baseball

2. suitcase

3. flashlight

4. backpack

5. bluebird

6. lunchbox

Write the last part of the compound word.
Write the compound word.

7. in side ——— inside

8. her self ——— herself

9. brain storm ——— brainstorm

10. out side ——— outside

Home Activity Your child spelled compound words. Have your child name the two words in each compound word.

© Pearson Education, Inc., 1

Adjectives for How Many and Articles

Some **adjectives** tell how many. The adjectives **a, an,** and **the** are called **articles**.

three dogs   **the** baby

Draw lines to match the words to the pictures.
Say each adjective in a sentence.

1. two cribs

2. four chairs

3. five pictures

4. three boys

5. a house

© Pearson Education, Inc., 1

School + Home

Home Activity Your child learned about adjectives for how many. Read a counting story with your child. Have your child point out the adjectives that tell how many and use his or her fingers to show how many each adjective describes.

Name _____

Letter Format

Dear _____ ,

_____

_____

_____

_____

_____

_____

_____

                    _____

                    _____ ,
                    _____

                    _____

Name _____

1 2 3 4 5

Trace and **write** the numbers.

1 1 1

2 2 2

3 3 3

4 4 4

5 5 5

Circle your best number in each line.

Copy the sentence. Leave the correct space between words.

Sue has a new blue suit.

_____

Check spacing of words.

Home Activity Your child practiced writing numbers 1, 2, 3, 4, 5 and sentences with words with *ew, ui,* and *eu.* Have your child practice writing the numbers one more time. Then write the following words on a sheet of paper and have your child rewrite them to make a sentence: *knew, I, was, it, and true. (I knew it was true.)*

Name _____

Alan sent this e-mail to his friends.
Help Alan record what he learned.

```
○○○
```

From: Alan
Subject: Your favorite treasure
Date: April 4

I want to find out your favorite treasure.

Please tell me what your favorite treasure is.

Favorite Treasures	
Stuffed Animal	ⵌ
Blanket	|||
Favorite Toy	||||
Gift from a Relative	ⵌ ||

ⵌ = 5

Make tally marks to show what Alan learned.

1. Five friends treasure a stuffed animal.

2. Three friends treasure a blanket.

3. Four friends treasure a favorite toy.

4. Seven friends treasure a gift from a relative.

Home Activity Your child learned how to write, send, and reply to an e-mail. If possible, help your child compose and send an e-mail to a family member.

Sue's Daydream

Compound Words		Vowel Digraphs *ue, ew, ui*		High-Frequency Words	
daydream	sunlight	Sue	crew	was	I
daydreaming	inside	true	Drew	a	to
onto	popcorn	blue	juice	the	
suitcase	everyone	new	cruise	they	
into	herself	flew		said	

Sue was in reading class,

but she wasn't reading.

It's true—Sue was daydreaming!

"Time for math!" said Miss Drew.

"I must quit daydreaming," Sue said to herself.

"But a cruise might be fun . . . ."

Decodable Story *Sue's Daydream*
Target Skills Compound Words; Vowel Digraphs *ue, ew, ui*

She got onto a plane with her
new suitcase.

The plane flew off into the blue
sky.

Sunlight streamed in.

The crew inside was nice.

"We've got juice and popcorn for
everyone," they said.

Name _____

Compound Words

Spelling Words

| backpack | outside | baseball | herself | flashlight |
| bluebird | lunchbox | suitcase | inside | brainstorm |

Read about some good friends. **Write** the missing list words.

High-Frequency Words

remember

picture

1. Ellie and I went o **utside** .

2. Ellie had a f **lashlight** .

3. We saw b **luebird** feathers.

4. We looked i **nside** a hollow tree.

5. Next, we played b **aseball** .

6. Then we got a snack out of my l **unchbox** .

7. We got juice out of Ellie's b **ackpack** .

8. Ellie drank three boxes of juice by h **erself** .

9. I still p **icture** Ellie and the juice.

10. It is fun to r **emember** her.

Home Activity Your child used spelling words to complete a story about friends. Ask your child to tell about a friend, using some of the list words.

© Pearson Education, Inc., 1

Spelling Compound Words **485**

Name _____

Adjectives for How Many and Articles

Look at the picture. **Complete** each sentence with an adjective from the box. **Say** a sentence for each article.

(a   two   three)

1. There are ___ **three** ___ people in this family.

2. There are ___ **two** ___ children.

3. There is ___ **a** ___ man.

Write about the people in your family.
Use adjectives that tell how many.

Possible answer: My family has two parents. There are three boys. There is a girl.

Home Activity Your child learned how to use adjectives for how many in writing. Place groups of one, two, three, four, and five pennies on a table and have your child write sentences about the groups using adjectives that tell how many.

Name _____

Compound Words

Connect two parts to make a list word.
Write the compound word.

1. in	storm	1.	**inside**
2. her	side	2.	**herself**
3. brain	light	3.	**brainstorm**
4. flash	self	4.	**flashlight**
5. suit	bird	5.	**suitcase**
6. blue	case	6.	**bluebird**

Spelling Words

backpack
outside
baseball
herself
flashlight
bluebird
lunchbox
suitcase
inside
brainstorm

Circle the word that is spelled correctly.

7. (lunchbox) lonchbox

8. owtside (outside)

9. (backpack) back pack

10. basball (baseball)

Home Activity Your child has been learning to spell compound words. Help your child brainstorm other compound words.

Name _____

Adjectives for How Many and Articles

Mark the sentence that has a line under the adjective.

1. ⊗ There are <u>ten</u> families in the park.
   ◯ There are ten <u>families</u> in the park.
   ◯ There are ten families in the <u>park</u>.

2. ◯ Four brothers <u>throw</u> a football.
   ◯ Four brothers throw a <u>football</u>.
   ⊗ <u>Four</u> brothers throw a football.

3. ◯ I see three <u>fathers</u> on a bench.
   ⊗ I see <u>three</u> fathers on a bench.
   ◯ I <u>see</u> three fathers on a bench.

4. ◯ Where <u>are</u> my two sisters?
   ◯ Where are my two <u>sisters</u>?
   ⊗ Where are my <u>two</u> sisters?

5. ⊗ <u>Six</u> children play tag on the grass.
   ◯ Six children <u>play</u> tag on the grass.
   ◯ Six children play tag on the <u>grass</u>.

6. ◯ There are five <u>mothers</u> with babies.
   ⊗ There are <u>five</u> mothers with babies.
   ◯ There are five mothers with <u>babies</u>.

Choose other adjectives. **Say** a sentence for each adjective.

Home Activity Your child prepared for taking tests on adjectives for how many. Together read a short, simple newspaper or magazine article. Have your child circle adjectives that tell how many.

Add -ly or -ful to the word in ( ).
Write the new word on the line.

nice + -ly = nice**ly**

(play)

1. The dog is **playful** .

(slow)

2. The dog walked **slowly** .

(quick)

3. Then it ran **quickly** !

(safe)

4. The dog got home **safely** .

(thank)

5. Miss Moon was **thankful** .

© Pearson Education, Inc., 1

Home Activity Your child added -ly and -ful to words. Ask your child to give you instructions using words with the -ly suffix, such as *Clap loudly; Talk softly; Walk quickly.* Follow the instructions. Then have your child write simple sentences using *playful* and *thankful.*

Name _____

Read the words in the box.
Pick a word to match each clue.
Write it on the line.

> across   because   dance   only   opened   shoes   told

1.

   opened

2.

   dance

3.

   across

4. She said, "I _____ you to read slowly."

   told

5. The plant grows _____ it has water.

   because

6. Mom said, "_____ one treat!"

   Only

7.

   shoes

 Home Activity Your child learned to read the words *across, because, dance, only, opened, shoes,* and *told.* Make up more clues for the words on this page. Ask your child to identify the words. Challenge your child to think of some clues.

© Pearson Education, Inc., 1

Name _____

Draw a line to match what happens with why it happens.

What Happens	Why It Happens

1.

2.

3.

4.

5.

Home Activity Your child learned about what happens (effect) and why it happens (cause). While watching a sporting event, such as a soccer game or swim meet, invite your child to identify what happens and why.

How to Make a Drum

First, get a coffee can with a plastic lid.

Next, color a piece of paper.

Wrap it around the coffee can.

Then give it to your friend.

See who can drum the loudest!

Key Features of Directions

· Directions give details about how to do something.

· Directions should be clear and easy to understand.

© Pearson Education, Inc., 1

School +Home

Home Activity Your child is learning to write simple directions for how to do something. Share an activity at home and discuss how to do it.

Name _____

Circle the word for each picture.

1.	2.	3.	4.
(zoo) zip	span (spoon)	pal (pool)	(stool) stale

5.	6.	7.	8.
(fruit) fool	gaze (goose)	(boot) bait	(spool) spill

Pick a word to finish each sentence.
Write the word in the sentence.

9. The __**moose**__ blocked the cars on the road.

   moose   mouse

10. I dropped my __**food**__ on the floor.

    farm   food

11. I used a __**broom**__ to clean up the mess.

    boot   broom

Home Activity Your child practiced reading and creating words with *oo* as in *moon*. Write the *oo* words from this page on scraps of paper. Have your child pick a word and use it in a sentence.

Name _____

Words with Suffixes *-ly*, *-ful*

Spelling Words				
slowly	careful	quickly	useful	painful
playful	sadly	gladly	nicely	wonderful

Write the list word that means the same as the underlined words.

1. She said good-bye <u>in a sad way</u>.

1. **sadly**

2. We had a <u>very good</u> time.

2. **wonderful**

3. Be <u>alert</u> when playing ball.

3. **careful**

4. The twins play <u>in a nice way</u>.

4. **nicely**

5. Her foot was <u>full of pain</u>.

5. **painful**

6. I will <u>be happy to</u> help.

6. **gladly**

7. The hamsters are <u>full of play</u>.

7. **playful**

8. Drive <u>in a slow way</u>.

8. **slowly**

9. My pen is still <u>full of use</u>.

9. **useful**

10. He finished his work <u>in a fast way</u>.

10. **quickly**

Home Activity Your child spelled words with the suffixes *-ly* and *-ful*. Ask your child to explain what each suffix means. (Suffix *-ly* means "in a ___ way." Suffix *-ful* means "full of ___.")

© Pearson Education, Inc., 1

Name _____

Adjectives That Compare

Add **-er** to an adjective to compare
two persons, places, or things.

The cat is **smaller** than the dog.

Add **-est** to an adjective to compare
three or more persons, places, or things.

The mouse is **smallest** of the three.

Circle the adjectives that compare two things.
Underline the adjectives that compare three or more things.

1. Mrs. Hopper is (taller) than Henry.

2. Henry's father is <u>tallest</u> of the three.

3. Mudge is (smarter) than that dog.

4. Mudge is the <u>smartest</u> dog of all.

5. Henry's mother is (older) than Henry.

6. Mrs. Hopper is the <u>oldest</u> of the three.

Home Activity Your child learned about adjectives that compare. Read a story with your child. Have your child look for adjectives that compare and tell what things are being compared.

Name _____

Sequence

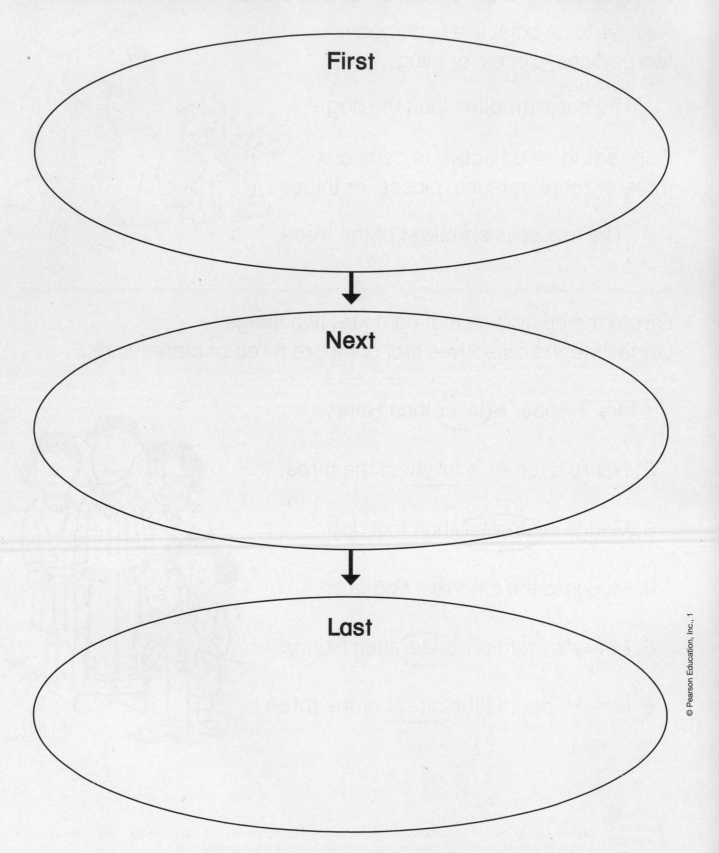

First

Next

Last

Name _____

6   7   8   9   10

Trace and **write** the numbers.

6   6   6

7   7   7

8   8   8

9   9   9

10   10   10

Circle your best number in each line.

Copy the sentence. Leave the correct space between words.

You can not be too helpful.

_____

_____

Home Activity Your child practiced writing numbers 6, 7, 8, 9, 10 and sentences with words with *-ly, -ful,* and *oo.* Have your child practice writing the numbers one more time. Then write the following words on a sheet of paper and have your child read and rewrite them as neatly as possible: *skillful, softly, broom.*

Name _____

Put each group of last names in ABC order.
Write the names on the lines.

Turza   Taylor   Terry   Till

1. **Taylor**

2. **Terry**

3. **Till**

4. **Turza**

Lin   Lewis   Lopez   Lance

5. **Lance**

6. **Lewis**

7. **Lin**

8. **Lopez**

Costello   Clifton   Cruz   Chang

9. **Chang**

10. **Clifton**

11. **Costello**

12. **Cruz**

School + Home

Home Activity Your child learned to use alphabetical order to find names in a phone book. The next time you need a phone number, ask your child to help you find the information.

Helping at a Zoo

Suffixes -ly, -ful	Vowel Sound in *moon: oo*		High-Frequency Words	
mainly	zoo	cool	a	some
quickly	bloom	soon	many	visit
likely	food	too	people	you
playful	broom	booth		
painful				

Many people help at a zoo.

Some mainly help flowers bloom.

Some get food for everyone.

You'll likely visit a zoo someday.

Will you go soon?

Will you help at a zoo too?

Decodable Story *Helping at a Zoo*
Target Skills Suffixes -ly, -ful; Vowel Sound in *moon: oo*

4

Some helpers use a broom all day.

Some helpers sell treats in a booth.

Some helpers keep playful hippos cool.

2

A vet helps at a zoo.

A cub might get a painful cut.

A vet quickly helps its cut heal.

3

Name _____

Words with Suffixes *-ly, -ful*

Spelling Words	High-Frequency Words
slowly careful quickly useful painful	because
playful sadly gladly nicely wonderful	across

Write the suffix *-ly* or *-ful*. **Write** the word.

1. I went glad **ly** .   **gladly**

2. The swimmers were care **ful** .   **careful**

3. It is a wonder **ful** party.   **wonderful**

4. A cell phone is very use **ful** .   **useful**

5. Mia plays nice **ly** .   **nicely**

6. We quick **ly** shut the door.   **quickly**

7. That's a play **ful** kitten.   **playful**

8. Cook the stew slow **ly** .   **slowly**

Write the words to complete this sentence.

I went 9. **across** the street 10. **because** I saw my friend.

Home Activity Your child used spelling words to complete sentences. Read a sentence and have your child spell the list word.

© Pearson Education, Inc., 1

Adjectives That Compare

Write about three special friends.
Use words from the box or your own
adjectives that compare.

| oldest   shorter   quieter   faster   tallest |

Possible answer: Bob is

shorter than Dan. Dan is

quieter than Wes. Dan is the

oldest of the three.

Home Activity Your child learned how to use adjectives that compare in writing. Talk about neighbors or family friends with your child. Together write sentences that compare two or more of these people. Use an adjective with *-er* or *-est* in each sentence.

© Pearson Education, Inc., 1

Name _____

Words with Suffixes *-ly, -ful*

Spelling Words				
slowly	careful	quickly	useful	painful
playful	sadly	gladly	nicely	wonderful

Circle the word that is spelled correctly.

1. (sadly)   sady   2. galadly   (gladly)

3. (quickly)   quikly   4. wondrful   (wonderful)

Write the list words in the puzzle.

Across
7. in a nice way
9. in a slow way
10. full of use

Down
5. full of pain
6. full of play
8. not careless

Puzzle:

Down 5: p a i n f u l

Across 7: n i c e l y

Down 8: c a r e f u l

Down 6: p l a y f u l

Across 9: s l o w l y

Across 10: u s e f u l

Home Activity Your child has been learning to spell words with the suffixes *-ly* and *-ful*. Say a base word. Ask your child to add *-ly* or *-ful* and say and spell the new word.

Adjectives That Compare

Mark the sentence that has a line under the adjective.

1. ⊗ Ms. Feld's lawn is <u>greener</u> than Mrs. Ho's lawn.
   ○ Ms. Feld's <u>lawn</u> is greener than Mrs. Ho's lawn.
   ○ Ms. Feld's lawn <u>is</u> greener than Mrs. Ho's lawn.

2. ○ <u>Mr. Jones</u> has the brownest lawn of all.
   ○ Mr. Jones <u>has</u> the brownest lawn of all.
   ⊗ Mr. Jones has the <u>brownest</u> lawn of all.

3. ○ Mr. Wyner's <u>trees</u> are shorter than Mrs. Garcia's trees.
   ⊗ Mr. Wyner's trees are <u>shorter</u> than Mrs. Garcia's trees.
   ○ Mr. Wyner's trees <u>are</u> shorter than Mrs. Garcia's trees.

4. ○ Mr. Scott has the tallest <u>trees</u> in the neighborhood.
   ○ Mr. Scott has the tallest trees in the <u>neighborhood</u>.
   ⊗ Mr. Scott has the <u>tallest</u> trees in the neighborhood.

5. ⊗ Our house is <u>older</u> than Mrs. Vin's house.
   ○ Our <u>house</u> is older than Mrs. Vin's house.
   ○ Our house is older <u>than</u> Mrs. Vin's house.

6. ○ <u>Dr. Ruiz</u> owns the newest house on our street.
   ⊗ Dr. Ruiz owns the <u>newest</u> house on our street.
   ○ Dr. Ruiz owns the newest house on our <u>street</u>.

Home Activity Your child prepared for taking tests on adjectives that compare. With your child, look through a newspaper or magazine article. Help your child circle adjectives that compare. Then discuss what each adjective is comparing.

© Pearson Education, Inc., 1

Name _____

Pick a word from the box to match each picture.
Write it on the line.

 cr**ow**n

cloud clown flower house

1.

cloud

2.

flower

3.

house

4.

clown

Unscramble the letters to make a word.

uodl **loud**   wtno **town**   tuo **out**

Pick a word to finish each sentence. **Write** it on the line.

5. The opposite of *in* is **out**.

6. The radio was too **loud**.

7. I like to shop in **town**.

 School + Home

Home Activity Your child read and wrote words with *ow* that have the vowel sound heard in *Crown*. Encourage your child to make a list of other words with *ow* that rhyme with *cow* and *brown*.

Phonics Diphthongs *ou, ow*   505

© Pearson Education, Inc., 1

Name _____

Read the words in the box.
Pick a word to finish each sentence. **Write** it on the line.
Remember to use a capital letter at the beginning of a sentence.

along behind eyes never pulling toward

---

1. The dogs walked **along** the wall.

2. The dogs stopped **behind** the puddle.

---

3. Mom is **pulling** the boy away.

4. **Never** pet a dog you do not know well.

---

5. The puppy ran **toward** its mother.

6. Its **eyes** were happy and bright.

 Home Activity Your child learned to identify and read the words *along, behind, eyes, never, pulling,* and *toward*. Ask your child to make up a puppet show using this week's words. Write out the script that your child dictates. Use paper bags or stick puppets to act it out.

© Pearson Education, Inc., 1

Name _____

Read the story.
Write the answer to each question.

Many weeks ago, Tony and Dad planted daisy seeds. They planted the seeds in a sunny part of a garden. Soon daisy plants were growing in the garden. The plants grew very tall with many daisies. One night it rained hard. Tony went out to the garden the next day. He felt so sad. All the plants were bent down. Then Dad came with sticks and string. He tied the plants to the sticks. Soon the plants were standing up!

I. Who are the characters in the story?

Tony and Dad

2. Where does the story happen?

in a garden

3. Why did Tony feel sad?

The plants were bent down.

4. Why did Dad tie the plants to sticks?

Dad wanted to make the plants stand up.

5. How do you think Tony feels at the end of the story?

happy

Home Activity Your child identified the characters, setting, and the problem and solution in a story. Together read a story that has an obvious problem and solution. Pause as you read to ask your child how the characters feel and why they feel that way.

Comprehension Character, Setting, and Plot **507**

Name _____

Cleaning Up

Bob and Sue were squirrels. They liked to play in the lot behind the hardware store. One day, a kid threw trash. Sue got angry.

Sue complained, "All this littering has to stop."

Bob said, "Yes. Let's get people to help clean."

Bob and Sue made signs for a cleanup on Saturday. They climbed trees and hung up the signs. On Saturday, many people showed up. No one knew who had the great idea to clean the lot. But everyone was glad to help. Now Bob and Sue have a great place to play!

Key Features of an Animal Fantasy

- characters are animals

- characters do things that real animals can't do

Circle the word for each picture.

 bott**le**

1.	2.	3.	4.

(cattle) canned | tabbed (table) | picking (pickle) | (turtle) turned

---

5.	6.	7.	8.

(candle) candy | needy (needle) | handy (handle) | (saddle) sadder

---

Find the word that has the same ending sound as .
Mark the ⬭ to show your answer.

9. ⬭ litter
   ⬭ lightly
   ⬛ little

10. ⬛ purple
    ⬭ purred
    ⬭ purest

Home Activity Your child read two-syllable words with -*le* in the second syllable. Have your child fold a sheet of paper into four boxes, choose four of the words he or she circled, find a rhyming word for that word, and draw pictures of the rhyming word. Ask your child to label each picture.

Name _____

Words with *ow*

Spelling Words				
how	town	down	now	brown
cow	clown	frown	crowd	growl

Name the picture. **Write** a list word.

1. **clown**   2. **town**   3. **cow**

Circle the correct word in the phrase. **Write** the word.

4. up and (down) cow   4. **down**

5. a (brown) frown cow   5. **brown**

6. town (how) about that   6. **how**

7. lost in the (crowd) down   7. **crowd**

8. the brown (growl) of the lion   8. **growl**

9. clown (now) and then   9. **now**

10. wipe off that (frown) down   10. **frown**

Home Activity Your child spelled words with the vowel sound in *how*. Ask your child to name two letters common to all the spelling words. (*ow*)

510 **Spelling** Words with *ow*

Imperative Sentences

An **imperative sentence** is a **command** sentence that tells someone to do something. It begins with a **capital letter.** It ends with a **period (.).**

Go to the garden.

Please watch the dog.

Underline each sentence that is a command.

I. Are you thirsty?

2. Pour a glass of milk.

3. You spilled some milk.

4. Please wipe up the milk.

5. Let me help you.

6. Drink your milk.

Home Activity Your child learned about commands. Explain how to play a game to your child. Have your child say "Command" each time he or she hears you use a command.

Name _____

Story Map

Characters

Setting

Events

Beginning

Middle

End

Home Activity Your child is writing a story with animal characters. Together make up or remember a story about animal characters.

Name _____

Trace and **write** the numbers.

Circle your best number in each line.

Copy the sentence. Leave the correct space between words.

The cow is in the stable.

_____
- - - - - - - - - - - - - - - - - - -
_____

Home Activity Your child practiced writing numbers 11, 12, 13, 14, 15 and sentences with words with *ou, ow,* and *-le.* Have your child practice writing the numbers one more time. Then have your child read and rewrite one of the sentences from above.

Name _____

When does a problem have a clever solution?

Step 1—Think about problems that you have to solve.

1. Write two or three problems.

Responses will vary.

Step 2—Choose a topic.

2. Write the problem that you want to try to solve.

Responses will vary.

Step 3—Formulate research questions.

3. Write two questions about the problem that you want to solve.

Responses will vary.

4. What sources of information can help you find creative ways to solve the problem?

Responses will vary.

Home Activity Your child learned how to generate topic ideas, formulate research questions, and choose reference sources. Talk to your child about problems around your home that need to be solved and help your child develop solutions.

© Pearson Education, Inc., 1

Chow

Diphthongs *ow* and *ou*		Final Syllable *-le*	High-Frequency Words
Chow	town	ground	little	was
how	growl	around	beagle	a
bow	stout	grouch	tumble	said
now	hound	sound	Mingle	I
howl	proud	loud	puddle	the
scowled	found		nibble	to
			chuckle	is

Chow was a stout little beagle.

"See how my hound can tumble and bow?" said Miss Mingle. "I am proud!"

Then Miss Mingle got Chow a treat.

"Nibble this," she said with a chuckle.

"Now we'll all feel better!"

Decodable Story *Chow*
Target Skills Diphthongs *ow* and *ou*, Final Syllable *-le*

Chow found a puddle on the ground.

He splashed mud all around.

"Now I am a grouch!" said Miss Mingle.

Chow started to howl.

"That sound is too loud," Miss Mingle scowled.

"Everyone in town will growl!"

Name _____

Words with *ow*

Spelling Words				
how	town	down	now	brown
cow	clown	frown	crowd	growl

High-Frequency Words
eyes
never

Write the missing list word.

1. We saw him milk a **cow** .

2. Don't get lost in the **crowd** .

3. Her hair is **brown** .

4. Do you know **how** to skate?

5. I heard the dog **growl** .

6. We have a park in our **town** .

7. Let's go **down** the slide.

8. The best time is **now** .

9. I closed my **eyes** .

10. I will **never** stop laughing.

Home Activity Your child wrote spelling words to complete sentences. Have your child spell a list word and use it in a sentence.

© Pearson Education, Inc., 1

Imperative Sentences

Pam has a problem with her cat.
What should Pam do?
Tell what Pam should do.
Write about your ideas.
Use commands.

Possible answer: Call to the cat. Show the cat some food. Get a ladder. Ask an adult to climb up.

Home Activity Your child learned how to use commands in writing. Ask your child to write about how to make a sandwich. Then have your child underline commands he or she used.

© Pearson Education, Inc., 1

Name _____

Words with *ow*

Spelling Words				
how	town	down	now	brown
cow	clown	frown	crowd	growl

Unscramble the letters. **Write** the list word.

1. l o c n w   1. **clown**

2. w o h   2. **how**

3. b n r o w   3. **brown**

4. w l g r o   4. **growl**

5. o w c   5. **cow**

6. n t w o   6. **town**

7. o n w   7. **now**

Write the missing words.

8. The **crowd** had to wait in a long line.

9. There was no place to sit **down** .

10. Everyone began to **frown** .

Home Activity Your child has been learning to spell words with the vowel sound in *how*. Give clues about a word. Ask your child to guess and spell the word.

© Pearson Education, Inc., 1

Imperative Sentences

Mark the sentence that has a command.

1. ⊗ Look in the newspaper.
    ○ Will you look in the newspaper?
    ○ Ben looks in the newspaper.

2. ○ Meg will find the answer.
    ⊗ Find the answer.
    ○ Did she find the answer?

3. ○ Cam left the key here.
    ○ Where is the key?
    ⊗ Please find the key.

4. ○ Will the glue hold the pieces together?
    ○ I will glue the pieces together.
    ⊗ Glue the pieces together.

5. ○ Who dropped the letter in the box?
    ⊗ Please drop the letter in the box.
    ○ Ann dropped the letter in the box.

6. ⊗ Look at this dirty shirt.
    ○ This shirt is dirty.
    ○ Why is this shirt dirty?

© Pearson Education, Inc., 1

 School + Home **Home Activity** Your child prepared for taking tests on commands. Together read a favorite story. Have your child point out commands, questions, and statements in the story.

520 Conventions Imperative Sentences

Name _____

Write a word from the box to match each picture.

| couch   cow   flour |
| snowman   towel   rowboat |

1.

couch

2.

rowboat

3.

cow

4.

flour

5.

snowman

6.

towel

Write the word to finish each sentence. **Remember** to use capital letters at the beginning of a sentence.

7. **How** does your garden grow? **how   have**

8. Can I come to play at your **house** ? **toy   house**

9. I like to **blow** bubbles. **blue   blow**

10. I went **outside** to take a walk. **outside   inside**

Home Activity Your child read and wrote words with vowel patterns *ou* as in *cloud,* and *ow* as in *cow* and *snow.* Encourage your child to make a list of words that rhyme with these vowel patterns.

Name _____

Read the words in the box.
Pick a word to finish each sentence.
Write it on the line.

door   loved   should   wood

Dear Jack,

I had such a good time at your house last week.

I ____**loved**____ it when we played in the snow!
Remember when we made an igloo?

We used a blanket for the ____**door**____, and it froze stiff.

You ____**should**____ come to my house!
It is very warm here even in the winter.

My dad and I are going to paint the ____**wood**____ rail.

Your friend,

Sam

Home Activity Your child learned to identify and read the words *door, loved, should,* and *wood.* Ask your child to write a story that uses each word and read it aloud.

Name _____

Read the story.
Write an answer to each question.

   Jean painted a picture of a vase with roses in it. Some of the roses were red. Some were yellow roses. The vase was blue. Jean took her picture to an art show. A man hung Jean's picture on a wall. Many people came to the show to see the pictures. Then Jean saw a blue tag on her picture. The man handed Jean the blue tag. All the people clapped.

1. Why do you think the people clapped?

Jean won a prize for her picture.

2. What do you think the blue tag means?

Jean won first place.

3. What do you think Jean will do next?

Possible answers: Jean will paint more pictures.

Jean will take another picture to an art show.

© Pearson Education, Inc., 1

Home Activity Your child used what he or she already knew about a situation to draw conclusions about an event. Reread the story with your child. Have your child tell you what he or she already knew about art shows that helped him or her draw conclusions about the story.

Comprehension Draw Conclusions **523**

Name _____

 Please, Mr. Wolf

Dear Mr. Wolf,

I have read a lot of books where you always seem to show up and cause trouble. It makes me angry to see you blow the pigs' houses down. What did they ever do to you?

It makes me sad to see you scare Little Red Riding Hood. She is just trying to get through the woods to see her grandma.

So, please Mr. Wolf, try to be nice and stop scaring people and ruining their homes.

Thank you,
Patrick

Key Features of a Letter to a Character

• describes feelings to a story character

• includes a friendly greeting and closing

Name _____

Circle the word for each picture.

1.
lesson (lemon)

2.
pillow (pilot)

3.
(bacon) basket

4.
wagging (wagon)

5.
(river) rigged

6.
(napkin) navel

7.
timber (tiger)

8.
came (camel)

Draw a picture for each word.

9. spider

Children's artwork should show a spider.

10. baby

Children's artwork should show a baby.

© Pearson Education, Inc., 1

School + Home

Home Activity Your child read words with two syllables that have one consonant in the middle. Have your child choose five words from the page and use each word in a sentence.

Mole and the Baby Bird

Phonics Syllables V/CV, VC/V   525

Name _____

Words with *ou*

Read the clue. **Write** the list word.

Spelling Words

Spelling Words
mouth
house
found
our
out
cloud
ouch
shout
round
count

It starts with **h**, and it rhymes with **mouse**.

1. **house**

It starts with **cl**, and it rhymes with **loud**.

2. **cloud**

It starts with **sh**, and it rhymes with **pout**.

3. **shout**

It starts with **o**, and it rhymes with **couch**.

4. **ouch**

Write the missing list word.

5. Look at **our** pups.

6. We **found** them last week.

7. Can you **count** them?

8. One pup wants to get **out** .

9. He put a ball in his **mouth** .

10. The ball is **round** .

Home Activity Your child spelled words with the vowel sound in *out*. Ask your child to name two letters common to all the spelling words. (*ou*)

Pronouns

A **pronoun** is a word that takes the place of a noun or nouns. The words **he, she, it, we, you,** and **they** are pronouns.

People see the bird.	**They** see the bird.
Jake helps the bird.	**He** helps the bird.

Circle the pronoun in each sentence.
Say a sentence for each pronoun.

1. (We) need to feed the birds.

2. (They) like to eat.

3. (He) likes the wild bird.

4. (It) can fly away.

Circle the pronoun in ( ) that takes the place of the underlined word or words.

5. This bird is little. (She, (It))

6. Mole and I went to the forest. (He, (We))

7. Mole gets food for the bird. ((He), They)

8. Mole and Grandad let the bird go. ((They), You)

Home Activity Your child learned about pronouns. Write *he, she, it, we, you,* and *they* in a list. Point to each word and ask your child to use it in a sentence.

© Pearson Education, Inc., 1

Name _____

Letter Format

Dear _____ ,

_____
- -
_____
- -
_____
- -
_____
- -
_____
- -
_____
- -
_____
- -

                              _____
                              - - - - - - - - - - -
                              _____ ,
                              - - - - - - - - - - -
                              _____

© Pearson Education, Inc., 1

School + Home

Home Activity Your child can express opinions about a story. Discuss a book you both have liked.

Name _____

Trace and **write** the numbers.

16   16   16

17   17   17

18   18   18

19   19   19

20   20   20

Copy the sentence. Leave the correct space between words.

The baby camel is cute.

_____
- - - - - - - - - - - - - -
_____

Did you leave the correct space between your words? | Yes | | No |

© Pearson Education, Inc., 1

Home Activity Your child practiced writing numbers *16, 17, 18, 19, 20* and words with short and long vowels. Have your child practice writing the numbers one more time. Then have your child read and rewrite the sentence from above.

Name _____

Read the numbered words in each list.
Match each numbered word with the guide
words that show where you would find the word in
a dictionary.
Draw a line from the numbered word to its guide words.

1. mouth   **A.** part/plant

2. picture   **B.** gerbil/goose

3. give   **C.** mouse/much

4. dance   **D.** damp/date

5. because   **E.** clam/cube

6. color   **F.** bark/beep

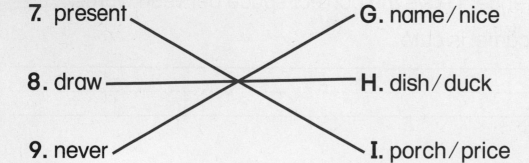

7. present   **G.** name/nice

8. draw   **H.** dish/duck

9. never   **I.** porch/price

School + Home   **Home Activity** Your child learned about using alphabetical order and guide words in a dictionary. Help your child look up other words in a dictionary at home.

Name _____

A New Home

Vowel Patterns *ow* (how)(show), *ou*			Syllables V/CV and VC/V		High-Frequency Words	
brown	windows	found	house	Toby's	city	a	is
now	throw	out		tiny	models	I	of
down	yellow			begin	comics	the	to
town	pillow			baby	closet	said	their
				label			

Toby's dad got a new job.

"I found a brown house in the city," he said.

"It is tiny, but it has lots of windows."

© Pearson Education, Inc., 1

Dad and Toby missed their house in town.

But Dad liked his new job, and Toby liked his shiny new closet!

Decodable Story *A New Home*
Target Skills Vowel Patterns ow (how, show), *ou*; Syllables V/CV and VC/V

"I'll begin to pack right now,"
said Toby.

"I'll throw out my yellow baby
pillow,

but I'll pack my models and
comics!"

2

"I'll label the boxes," said Dad.

"We'll take them down to the
truck."

3

Name _____

Words with *ou*

Spelling Words				
mouth	house	found	our	out
cloud	ouch	shout	round	count

High-Frequency Words
loved
should

Read about finding bugs. **Write** the missing list words.

1. We **found** some bugs.

2. They are **round** .

3. Let's **count** them.

4. One got in my **mouth** .

5. Did you **shout** ?

6. I said **ouch** .

7. I spit it **out** .

8. Look at that **cloud** !

9. The bugs **should** not be here.

10. No one **loved** these bugs.

School + Home **Home Activity** Your child used spelling words and high-frequency words to complete sentences. Read a sentence on this page. Have your child spell the list word.

© Pearson Education, Inc., 1

Pronouns

Look at the picture.
Write about what the people are doing.
Use pronouns.

Possible answer: They see birds. She sees a squirrel. He points over the hill.

Find other pronouns. **Say** a sentence for each pronoun.

Home Activity Your child learned how to use pronouns in writing. With your child, look through a family photo album. Talk about what you see in the photos, using pronouns instead of names.

© Pearson Education, Inc., 1

Name _____

Words with *ou*

Spelling Words				
mouth	house	found	our	out
cloud	ouch	shout	round	count

Write the words in the puzzle.

1. m o u t h
2. o u t
3. o u c h
4. c l o u d

cloud
ouch
out
mouth

Connect the matching list words.

5. found

6. round

7. our

9. shout

8. house

found

house

10. count

count

shout

our

round

Home Activity Your child has been learning to spell words with the vowel sound in *out*. Draw a big butterfly. Have your child write the list words on the wings.

© Pearson Education, Inc., 1

Name _____

Pronouns

Mark the pronoun that can replace each underlined word or words.

1. <u>Birds</u> can fly.
   - ○ **A** He
   - ○ **B** It
   - ⊗ **C** They

2. <u>A mole</u> is an animal.
   - ⊗ **A** It
   - ○ **B** She
   - ○ **C** You

3. <u>Mole and I</u> feed the bird.
   - ○ **A** It
   - ⊗ **B** We
   - ○ **C** She

4. <u>Ann</u> plays with the bird.
   - ⊗ **A** She
   - ○ **B** They
   - ○ **C** We

5. <u>Rob</u> makes a nest.
   - ○ **A** They
   - ⊗ **B** He
   - ○ **C** It

Say a sentence for each pronoun.

Home Activity Your child prepared for taking tests on pronouns. Together look through a newspaper or magazine article. Take turns finding and circling the pronouns *he, she, it, we, you,* and *they.*

Name _____

Circle the word for each picture.

1. had (hood)

2. (cook) coat

3. (hook) hard

4. wide (wood)

5. pooch (pouch)

6. (look) lock

7. store (stood)

8. (brook) brake

Read the words in the box.
Circle the words that have the same vowel sound as .
Pick one of these words to finish each sentence.

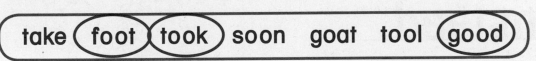

take (foot) (took) soon goat tool (good)

9. He _____ **took** _____ a picture of the lake.

10. That was a _____ **good** _____ joke.

11. My _____ **foot** _____ hurts.

© Pearson Education, Inc., 1

Home Activity Your child read and wrote words with *oo* that have the vowel sound heard in *foot*. Encourage your child to make lists that sort the words into those that rhyme with *took* and those that rhyme with *good*.

Phonics Vowel Sound in *foot: oo*   **537**

Name _____

Read the sentence. Unscramble the letters.
Write the word on the line. Remember to use
a capital letter at the beginning of a sentence.

among   another   instead   none

1. I will have **ahernot**.

another

2. **eNon** of the fruit is left.

None

3. Eat this **ineadst**.

instead

4. He likes to nap **angmo** his dogs.

among

Home Activity Your child learned to identify and read the words *among, another, instead,* and *none.* Write sentences such as these: *Is there another towel like this one? Try this one instead. None of the pie is left.* Leave a blank where the word should be, and have your child fill it in.

538   High-Frequency Words

© Pearson Education, Inc., 1

Name _____

Read the story. **Look** at the pictures.

Circle the answer to each question.

Chick and Spot are friends. They do not fight. They like to play games. Sometimes, they chase each other around the yard. I laugh when I watch them play.

1. Who is big?   **Spot**   Chick

2. Who is small?   Spot   **Chick**

3. Who can bark?   **Spot**   Chick

4. Who is standing?   Spot   **Chick**

5. Who has wings?   Spot   **Chick**

6. **Draw** two cats that look the same.

7. **Draw** two cats that do not look the same.

[Children's artwork should show two cats that are the same.]

[Children's artwork should show two cats that differ.]

© Pearson Education, Inc., 1

Home Activity Your child compared and contrasted characters in a story. As you read stories with your child, have him or her compare the characters in the stories.

Comprehension Compare and Contrast   **539**

Name _____

 Animals in Africa

What animals can I see in Africa?

When do giraffes sleep?

How much does an elephant weigh?

A male elephant weighs about 12,000 pounds. A female elephant weighs about 7,000 pounds.

Key Features of Questions

· Many *start* with the words **who, what, where, when,** or **how.**

· Questions end with a question mark.

© Pearson Education, Inc., 1

Name _____

Add -s, -ed, or **-ing** to the word in ( ).
Write the new word on the line.

(hope + -s)

1. Jean __**hopes**__ to grow corn.

(slope + -ing)

2. She plants seeds on the __**sloping**__ hill.

(care + -ed)

3. Jean __**cared**__ for the plants.

(taste + -ed)

4. Jean __**tasted**__ the corn.

(smile + -ing)

5. She is __**smiling**__ .

 Home Activity Your child added -s, -ed, or -ing to verbs that end in e. Write hope, slope, care, taste, and smile on a sheet of paper. Ask your child to tell the rule about adding -s, -ed, or -ing to each word. Then write the new words.

© Pearson Education, Inc., 1

Name _____

Words with *oo*

Circle the words in the box that rhyme. **Write** them.

foot   (took)
(look)   pool

1. **took**

2. **look**

foot   (moon)
book   (noon)

3. **moon**

4. **noon**

Spelling Words
book
moon
took
food
look
pool
zoo
noon
good
foot

Write a word that often goes with the list word.

5. bad

5. **good**

6. hand

6. **foot**

7. drink

7. **food**

Write the missing list word.

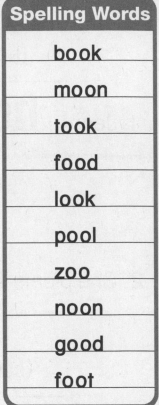

8. Greg wants to read a **book** .

9. Ann wants to swim at the **pool** .

10. Joe wants to feed deer at the **zoo** .

Home Activity Your child spelled words with the vowel sounds in *book* and *moon*. Ask your child to pronounce each list word and identify the vowel sound.

Pronouns *I* and *Me*

The pronouns **I** and **me** take the place of your name. Use I in the subject of a sentence. Use **me** after an action verb. Always write I with a capital letter.

Dot calls **me**. I talk to her.

When you talk about yourself and another person, name yourself last.

Jabber and I talk on the phone. Dot calls Jabber and **me**.

Write **I** or **me** to complete each sentence.

1. _____**I**_____ see an acorn.

2. It gives _____**me**_____ an idea.

3. _____**I**_____ take the acorn home.

4. Dot and _____**I**_____ paint it.

5. See Dot and _____**me**_____ hide the acorn.

Home Activity Your child learned about using *I* and *me*. Take turns telling about ways you use the telephone. Use *I* and *me* as you talk.

© Pearson Education, Inc., 1

Name _____

Topics for Questions

Questions

1. _____
_____
_____

2. _____
_____
_____

3. _____
_____
_____

Home Activity Your child can write questions and answers. Talk with your child about questions that interest each of you.

© Pearson Education, Inc., 1

Name _____

Copy the **sentences**. Leave the correct space between words.

I. We hoped mom baked.

_____

We hoped mom baked.

_____

2. I am taking this book.

_____

I am taking this book.

_____

3. They smiled at us.

_____

They smiled at us.

_____

4. He is judging a contest.

_____

He is judging a contest.

_____

5. We liked making juice.

_____

We liked makng juice.

_____

Did you leave the correct space between your words?   Yes   No

Home Activity Your child practiced writing sentences with words with added endings such as *-ed* and *-ing*. Write these words on a sheet of paper: *hide, ride, shine*. Have your child copy each word Dot then drop the *e* and add *-ing* to write the new word.

Name _____

Read the article. **Write** the answers.

Acorns

Acorns are <u>nuts</u>. They are the fruit of the **oak** tree. They fall to the ground in the FALL.

Who Eats Acorns

- Squirrels
- Mice
- Birds

The squirrel often buries his acorns. He eats them in the WINTER.

1. What is the title of the article? _____ **Acorns** _____

2. Use the picture to write a sentence about squirrels.

_____

<u>**Possible response: Squirrels bury acorns and eat them in winter.**</u>

_____

3. Write a heading from the article. **Who Eats**

Acorns _____

4. Which words are all capitals? **FALL, WINTER**

Home Activity Your child learned about text features. Look through nonfiction books with your child. Have your child point out text features, such as titles, subheads, and words that are all capitals or are in italics or boldface.

Going for a Drive

Vowel Sound in *foot: oo*	Drop Final *e* to Add Endings		High-Frequency Words	
stood	smiling	saving	was	what
good	driving	piling	a	to
shook	taking	riding	said	I
cookies	baking	waving	their	go
cookbook	writing		the	
look				

Dad was smiling. He stood up.

"It's a good day for driving," he said.

"I'm taking everyone with me. Let's go!"

1

"We're piling in the car and riding downtown," said Dad, waving at the kids.

"I know just the place to go!"

4

Decodable Story *Going for a Drive*
Target Skills Vowel Sound in *foot: oo*; Drop Final e to Add Endings

Lacy and Mike shook their heads.

"We're baking cookies, but we can't find the cookbook."

Jon and Margo shook their heads.

"We're writing about saving the whales, but we don't know what to look up."

Name _____

Words with *oo*

Spelling Words				
book	moon	took	food	look
pool	zoo	noon	good	foot

High-Frequency Words
instead
another

Choose a word to finish the sentence.
Fill in the circle. **Write** the word.

1. I ● took ○ look ○ foot a sack lunch. _took_

2. Read the ○ took ○ zoo ● book. _book_

3. My ● foot ○ noon ○ took got wet. _foot_

4. We need more ○ noon ● food ○ look. _food_

5. Bears are at the ● zoo ○ moon ○ foot. _zoo_

6. That is ○ look ● good ○ took news. _good_

7. We swim in the ○ noon ○ foot ● pool. _pool_

8. The ○ look ○ took ● moon is bright. _moon_

Write the word that matches each clue.

9. in- _instead_   10. an- _another_

School + Home **Home Activity** Your child wrote spelling words and high-frequency words to complete sentences. Have your child create a sentence using three or more list words.

© Pearson Education, Inc., 1

Pronouns *I* and *Me*

Answer the question.
Change the words to write the answer.

Can I solve the mystery?

I can solve the mystery.

Write sentences about a mystery you solved.
Use I and **me.**

_____

Accept all resonable responses.

_____

_____

_____

_____

_____

Home Activity Your child learned how to use *I* and *me* in writing. Have your child read aloud the sentences he or she wrote on this page. Ask your child to point out the *I*'s and *me*'s.

© Pearson Education, Inc., 1

Name _____

Words with *oo*

Write the missing letters.

1. m **oo** n

2. b **oo** k

3. f **oo** t

4. p **oo** l

Spelling Words

book
moon
took
food
look
pool
zoo
noon
good
foot

Write the list words in the puzzle.

Across

6. 12:00
8. you eat this
10. see

Down

5. not bad
7. opposite of **gave**
9. animals live there

Puzzle:

5. g
6. n o o n
7. t / o
8. f o o d
9. z / o
10. l o o k
o

© Pearson Education, Inc., 1

School + Home

Home Activity Your child has been learning to spell words with the vowel sounds in *book* and *moon*. Write *oo* and pronounce a list word. Have your child add letters to spell the word. Continue with other list words.

Pronouns *I* and *Me*

Mark the letter of the word or words that complete each sentence.

1. _____ saw a squirrel.
   ○ Dad and me
   ⊗ Dad and I
   ○ Me

2. _____ found an acorn.
   ○ Me
   ○ Dad and me
   ⊗ I

3. Jabber asks _____ for clues.
   ⊗ Dot and me
   ○ Dot and I
   ○ I

4. _____ put the acorn in a hole.
   ○ Dot and me
   ○ Me
   ⊗ Dot and I

5. It was clever of _____ to solve the mystery.
   ○ I
   ⊗ me
   ○ me and I

Home Activity Your child prepared for taking tests on using *I* and *me*. Ask your child to read the sentences on this page and to say the word or words that complete each sentence as he or she reads it.

Name _____

Circle the word for each picture.

 t**oy**   s**oi**l

1.

(coins)   canes

2.

bay   (boy)

3.

(boil)   bail

4.

(joy)   jay

5.

boil   (book)

6.

all   (oil)

7.

(foil)   fail

8.

round   (royal)

Pick a word to finish each sentence. **Write** the word in the sentence.

9. May I _____**join**_____ you for lunch?   (jolly, join)

10. My favorite _____**toy**_____ is a racing car.   (tray, toy)

11. The meat will _____**spoil**_____ in the hot sun.   (spoil, spool)

Home Activity Your child read and wrote words with *oi* and *oy* as heard in *toy* and *soil*. Have your child sort the *oi* and *oy* words on this page and make two lists. Then have him or her read the words aloud.

Name _____

Read the words in the box.
Pick a word to finish each sentence.
Write it in the puzzle.

| against | goes | heavy | kinds | today |

I. We push the umbrella _____ the wind.

2. The rain _____ into our shoes.

3. We play all _____ of games in the big puddles!

4. Rain this _____ does not happen often.

The crossword puzzle:

1. **a**
2. **g o e s**
   a
   i
3. **k i n d s**
   s
4. **h**
   e
   a
   v
5. **t o d a y**

5. We will need dry socks _____ !

Home Activity Your child learned to read the words *against, goes, heavy, kinds,* and *today.* Ask your child to use the words in a silly song. Write the words of the song and invite him or her to illustrate it.

Name _____

Read the story.
Circle the sentence that tells what the story is all about.
Draw a picture of what the story is about.

1. The ground felt soft under my feet. The trees were tall and green. The air was warm. (I liked) (hiking in the forest.)

2.
Children's drawing should show a child walking in a setting that shows trees and woods.

Read the title of the story.
Circle a detail that might be in the story.
Draw a picture of that detail.

3. Title: The Party
(Jen and Fran sang)
("Happy Birthday")
Jen and Fran have bikes
Jen and Fran like school.

4.
Children's drawings should show two girls singing.

© Pearson Education, Inc., 1

Home Activity Your child learned about the main idea and details of a story. As you read stories with your child, have your child tell you what the story is all about. Have your child tell you details from the story.

Comprehension Main Idea and Details **555**

Name _____

You Need a Computer!

Everyone needs a computer!

A computer can help you find information.

You can find facts about your favorite animal.

A computer can help you stay in touch.

You can use it to send an e-mail to a friend.

You can use a computer to buy things.

You can even use it to watch a movie.

Buy a computer today!

Key Features of an Advertisement

- An advertisement promotes a product or a service.

- An advertisement describes the product or service.

Name _____

Write a word from the box
to match each picture.

 work**er**

| baker   sailor   painter   teacher |

1.

painter

2.

sailor

3.

baker

4.

teacher

Draw a picture of each word.

5. driver

Children's artwork should show a person driving.

6. actor

Children's artwork should show a person acting.

 Home Activity Your child read and wrote words that end in *-er* and *-or* as in *worker* and *actor*. Write each word on a slip of paper. Have your child choose a slip and act out the word for you to guess.

Name _____

Words with *oi, oy*

Spelling Words				
oil	soil	voice	point	boy
boil	coin	oink	toy	join

Circle the rhyming words in each row. **Write** them.

toy (oil) (boil)   1. **oil**   2. **boil**

(coin) (join) boil   3. **coin**   4. **join**

(toy) soil (boy)   5. **toy**   6. **boy**

Read the sentence. **Write** a list word that means the same as the underlined word.

7. Do you hear the big pig <u>squeal</u>?   7. **oink**

8. The farmer's <u>sound</u> is loud.   8. **voice**

9. The post has a sharp <u>end</u>.   9. **point**

10. The <u>ground</u> is very muddy.   10. **soil**

© Pearson Education, Inc., 1

School + Home

Home Activity Your child spelled words with the vowel sound in *boy* spelled *oi* and *oy*. Ask your child to pronounce each list word, spell it, and then check the spelling.

More About Pronouns

A **pronoun** can take the place of some words in a sentence.
I, you, he, she, it, we, and **they** are used in the **naming part** of a sentence. **Me, you, him, her, it, us,** and **them** are used in the **action part** of a sentence.

Ben likes **machines**. **He** makes **them**.

Write the pronoun in ( ) that can take the place of the underlined word or words.

1. <u>Sara</u> uses a lever. (Him, She)   **She**

2. <u>Pulleys</u> are all around. (They, Them)   **They**

3. <u>Ben</u> helps Sara. (He, Him)   **He**

4. <u>Sara</u> sees the machines. (She, Her)   **She**

5. Sara likes <u>the machines</u>. (them, they)   **them**

6. I like <u>Ben's machine</u>. (her, it)   **it**

Home Activity Your child learned more about pronouns. Ask your child to make up new sentences using the pronouns he or she wrote on this page.

Name _____

Web B

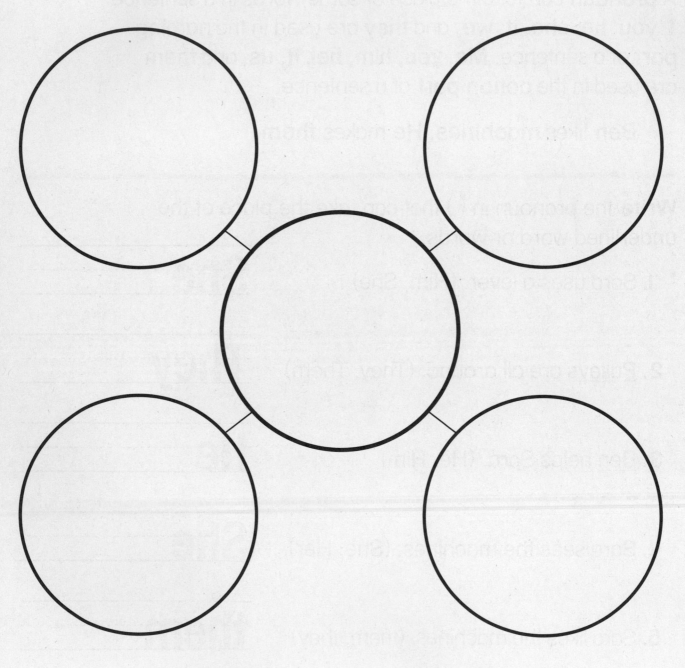

School + Home **Home Activity** Your child can write about topics such as machines. Discuss machines in your home and good ways to use them.

Name _____

Copy the **sentences.** Leave the correct space between words.

I. The boy is noisy.

The boy is noisy.

2. We lost the coin.

We lost the coin.

3. I did enjoy it.

I did enjoy it.

4. Roy is a good baker.

Roy is a good baker.

5. My dad is a sailor.

My dad is a sailor.

Did you leave the correct space between your words? | Yes | | No |

Home Activity Your child practiced writing sentences with words with *oy, oi, er,* and *or.* Write these words on a sheet of paper: *boil, corn, Mother, will, the.* Have your child rewrite the words to make a sentence. (*Mother will boil the corn.*)

Name _____

Amy asked her friends which invention they liked the most.
Help Amy complete the picture graph.

Favorite Inventions

1. Eight friends like cars the most. **Draw** eight cars on the picture graph.

2. Seven friends like television the most. **Draw** seven televisions on the picture graph.

3. Three friends like telephones the most. **Draw** three telephones on the picture graph.

4. Five friends like computers the most. **Draw** five computers on the picture graph.

5. One friend likes airplanes the most. **Draw** one airplane on the picture graph.

Home Activity Your child learned to make a picture graph. Together, make a picture graph that shows information about your family, such as favorite foods or favorite hobbies of each family member.

Name _____

What Are You?

Diphthongs oi, oy	Suffixes -er, -or		High-Frequency Words
soil	reader	singer	a
coins	writer	actor	are
boy	talker	baker	you
toy	dreamer	maker	do
joy	runner	farmer	the
	skater	banker	many

You're a boy or girl.

You're a reader and writer.

You're a talker and dreamer.

You are good at many things.

Try new things.

Keep doing the things that bring you joy!

Decodable Story *What Are You?*
Target Skills Diphthongs *oi, oy;* Suffixes *-er, -or*

Do you like the soil?

Do you collect coins?

Will you be a farmer or a banker?

2

Are you a fast runner or skater?

Are you a good singer or actor?

Are you a baker or toy maker?

3

Name _____

Words with *oi, oy*

Spelling Words				
oil	soil	voice	point	boy
boil	coin	oink	toy	join

High-Frequency Words
heavy
against

Circle a word to finish the sentence. **Write** the word.

1. Cover the seeds with (soil) toy.

2. He put a **voice** (coin) in his bank.

3. I will **boil** (point) to the answer.

4. Is this wagon your **soil** (toy)?

5. The pigs began to (oink) coin.

6. Did you **voice** (join) the club?

7. I saw a (boy) oil in the hall.

8. She spoke in a soft **coin** (voice).

9. Put the bike (against) heavy the wall.

10. The rock was so **against** (heavy).

soil

coin

point

toy

oink

join

boy

voice

against

heavy

Home Activity Your child wrote spelling words and high-frequency words to complete sentences. Have your child identify and spell the five list words that are most difficult for him or her.

© Pearson Education, Inc., 1

More About Pronouns

Imagine you are using a machine.
Write about what happens.
Use the pronouns **it**, **he**, **him**, **she**, **her**, **I**, **me**, **we**, or **us**.

Possible response: My sister and I make a machine. It helps us clean our rooms fast. It picks up all the toys and clothes.

Home Activity Your child learned how to use pronouns in writing. Take turns with your child writing sentences using the pronouns listed on this page.

566 Conventions More About Pronouns

Name _____

Words with *oi, oy*

Write these words in ABC order.

| soil |
| voice |
| point |
| toy |

 1. **point**

 2. **soil**

3. **toy**

4. **voice**

Use this code. **Write** the words.

5. **oil**

6. **coin**

7. **boy**

8. **join**

9. **oink**

10. **boil**

 Home Activity Your child has been learning to spell words with the vowel sound in *boy* spelled *oi* and *oy*. Help your child brainstorm other words with *oi* and *oy*.

© Pearson Education, Inc., 1

More About Pronouns

Mark the pronoun that can replace the underlined word or words.

1. The young girl has many ideas.
   - ⊗ She
   - ○ Them
   - ○ We

2. Her mother asks Sara about her plan.
   - ○ he
   - ○ she
   - ⊗ her

3. Sara sees a big mess.
   - ○ her
   - ⊗ it
   - ○ you

4. Sara's friends help her clean.
   - ○ Them
   - ○ He
   - ⊗ They

5. Her plan surprises the neighbors.
   - ⊗ them
   - ○ they
   - ○ we

© Pearson Education, Inc., 1

Home Activity Your child prepared for taking tests on pronouns. Read aloud a favorite storybook to your child. Ask your child to say "Stop" each time he or she hears a pronoun and to identify the pronoun.

Name _____

Circle the word for each picture.

 s<u>aw</u>   <u>au</u>to

1.	**2.**	**3.**	**4.**
pail (paw)	(yawn) yard	lunch (launch)	stray (straw)
5.	**6.**	**7.**	**8.**
false (faucet)	(crawl) call	lane (lawn)	(laundry) landed

Pick a word to finish each sentence. **Circle** the word.
Write the word in the sentence.

9. I like pasta with __**sauce**__ .

      (sauce) sash

10. The bear used his __**claw**__ to open the bag.

      clay (claw)

© Pearson Education, Inc., 1

School + Home **Home Activity** Your child read words with the vowel sounds *aw* and *au* as heard in *saw* and *auto*. Have your child make silly rhyming sentences using words that rhyme with *saw*. Example: *The cat can draw with her paw.*

Name _____

Read the sentence.
Unscramble the letters.
Write the word on the line.

| built early learn science through |

1. Many boys and girls like **sciceen**. **science**

2. We **lnear** about plants. **learn**

3. We get up **earyl** to see the

sun rise. **early**

4. We **uiltb** a little car! **built**

5. We look **ourghth** the glass. **through**

 Home Activity Your child learned to identify and read the words *built*, *early*, *learn*, *science*, and *through*. Find children's books about famous scientists and mathematicians. Read them together and challenge your child to find the words in the text.

© Pearson Education, Inc., 1

Name _____

Read the story. **Follow** the directions.

Mr. Lee's class is going on a trip. (First) they all get on the bus. It is going to be a fun day. (Then) the class gets off the bus at Rock Park Zoo. Rock Park Zoo is a big zoo. (Next) the class walks to the snake house.

_____

I. **Circle** words in the story that help you know the order of events.

2. **Write** I, 2, 3 to show the order of story events.

The class gets on the bus.   **1**

The class walks to the snake house.   **3**

The class gets off the bus   **2**

3. **Draw** a picture of what might happen next. Then **retell** the story in correct order.

[Possible drawing: Picture of children inside a zoo snake house looking at snakes.]

© Pearson Education, Inc., 1

Home Activity Your child identified order words and used them to put story events in the correct order. Have your child use order words to tell you what he or she does in the morning.

Comprehension Sequence **571**

Name _____

Writing Prompt: Think about something great that happened to you. Now write an autobiography that tells about it.

 The Best Day

Last year I was with Mom in a store. A lady asked me to be in a TV ad for the store. I happily said yes. The next day, Mom took me to the store. The lady was there. She told me what to do. She said I should act normally. We practiced for the ad. Then we quickly taped it. The ad was on TV! Soon my family and friends saw it.

© Pearson Education, Inc., 1

Name _____

Circle the word that names each picture.

1.

platter (painter) painting

2.

(toyshop) trays toolbox

3.

nose nothing (noisemaker)

4.

another awning (author)

Write the word from the box to finish each sentence.

| oatmeal | endpoint | inventor | boyhood |

5. A bowl of hot **oatmeal** is good for you.

6. Alexander Bell was a great **inventor**.

7. He had a great **boyhood**.

8. A dot at the end of a line is an **endpoint**.

© Pearson Education, Inc., 1

Home Activity Your child read compound words with vowel diphthongs (oi, oy) and vowel digraphs (oa), and words that end in –er and –or. Have your child read the following words aloud and then make up a sentence for each: teacher, actor, boyhood, and topsoil.

Name _____

Words with *aw*

Write a list word that belongs in the group.

1. jay, eagle, **hawk**

2. hammer, sandpaper, **saw**

3. skull, ribs, **jaw**

4. skip, walk, **crawl**

5. paint, sketch, **draw**

6. rule, order, **law**

Spelling Words
saw
draw
crawl
straw
law
jaw
paw
lawn
yawn
hawk

Write the missing word.

7. I sat on the **lawn** .

8. My dog sat on some **straw** .

9. He put his **paw** on my leg.

10. We both began to **yawn** .

Home Activity Your child spelled words with the vowel sound in *saw*. Have your child name the two letters common to all the spelling words (*aw*).

Adverbs

I learned a song **today.**
Today tells when.

Aleck worked on his invention **downstairs.**
Downstairs tells where.

Circle the adverb in each sentence that tells when or where.
Say a new sentence for each adverb.

1. Aleck got sick often.

2. Aleck went away to get better.

3. I built my invention yesterday.

4. I thought a lot about it before.

5. I got a good idea recently.

6. I will work on it next.

School + Home **Home Activity** Your child learned about adverbs that tell when and where. With your child, make a list of all the adverbs you can think of that tell when and where.

Autobiography
Top-Score Response

Focus/Ideas	A good autobiography tells about real events in the author's life.
Organization	A good autobiography is told in time order.
Voice	A good autobiography tells how the author feels about the events.
Word Choice	A good autobiography uses words that tell how, when, or where events happened.
Sentences	A good autobiography uses sentences that work together to tell the writer's ideas.
Conventions	A good autobiography uses words like **I** and **me**.

© Pearson Education, Inc., 1

Home Activity Your child is learning how writers tell events in their own lives. Have your child tell you about an event from his or her life.

Name _____

Copy the **sentences.** Leave the correct space between words.

I. Laura has a new shawl.

Laura has a new shawl.

2. We saw the vault.

We saw the vault.

3. Maureen made sauce.

Maureen made sauce.

4. I saw a drawing.

I saw a drawing.

5. The baby can crawl.

The baby can crawl.

Did you leave the correct space between your words? Yes No

School +Home **Home Activity** Your child practiced writing sentences with words with *aw* and *au*. Have your child choose one sentence to copy on a separate sheet of paper.

Name _____

Look at the Web page.
Answer the questions.

Click on a picture to learn more.

car   television   oven

1. Which button would you click on to look at the page you

looked at before this one? __**Back**__

2. Which picture would you click on to make a paper copy of the

information on this page? **the printer**

3. What is the address of this page?

www.url.here

4. What is the title of this page? **Inventions**

5. What would you do to learn more about ovens?

Click on the oven.

Home Activity Your child learned about using a Web page to find information. When you and your child are online, discuss how to navigate the Web.

Paul Bunyan

Vowel Sound aw, au	Syllable Patterns: Compound Words/ Suffixes		High Frequency Words	
Paul	boyhood	sailboats	a	of
sawed	football	oatmeal	was	other
yawned	worker	seacoast	as	do
Paul's			the	
dawn				
straw				

People tell tall tales about Paul Bunyan.

Paul had quite a boyhood.

His room was as big as ten football fields.

1

Paul had a blue ox named Babe.

Babe ate thirty bales of straw for a snack.

What other tall tales do people tell?

4

Decodable Story *Paul Bunyan*
Target Skills Vowel Sound *aw, au;* Syllable Patterns: Compound Words/Suffixes

Paul liked to look at the seacoast.

When Paul yawned, he slurped the sailboats right out of the sea.

Paul ate nine bathtubs of oatmeal each dawn.

Then Paul and his dad sawed wood.

Paul was a hard worker.

Name _____

Words with *aw*

Spelling Words				
saw	draw	crawl	straw	law
jaw	paw	lawn	yawn	hawk

High-Frequency Words
science
through

Write the missing list word.

1. The _____ says to wear seatbelts.

2. The baby is learning to _____.

3. Did you mow the _____?

4. Look at that _____ fly.

5. My _____ is sore.

6. Let's _____ a picture.

7. We _____ a snake.

8. My cat has one white _____.

9. Sue drank _____ a straw.

10. I like to study _____.

law

crawl

lawn

hawk

jaw

draw

saw

paw

through

science

Home Activity Your child wrote spelling words and high-frequency words to complete sentences. Help your child make silly sentences by substituting other list words in the sentences. For example: The **hawk** says to wear seatbelts.

Adverbs

Write about a time you built or made something.
Use **adverbs** to tell when and where.
Read your story aloud to the class.

Possible response: My grandma and I made a birdhouse last year. We hung it high in a tree. Now we sit outside and watch the birds.

Choose other adverbs. **Say** a sentence for each adverb.

Home Activity Your child learned how to use adverbs in writing. Have your child read aloud the story he or she wrote on this page. Ask your child to point out the adverbs.

Words with *aw*

Spelling Words				
saw	draw	crawl	straw	law
jaw	paw	lawn	yawn	hawk

Draw lines through all the **p**'s and **o**'s.
Write the word that is left.

1. h ~~o~~ a ~~p~~ w ~~p~~ k ~~o~~   1. **hawk**

2. l ~~o~~ ~~o~~ a ~~p~~ w ~~p~~ n   2. **lawn**

3. ~~p~~ c ~~o~~ r ~~p~~ a w ~~p~~ l   3. **crawl**

4. y ~~o~~ a ~~p~~ w ~~p~~ ~~p~~ n ~~o~~   4. **yawn**

Write six list words that rhyme with **thaw**.

5. **saw**   6. **law**

7. **draw**   8. **jaw**

9. **straw**   10. **paw**

Home Activity Your child has been learning to spell words with the vowel sound in *saw*. Help your child use the list words to make more word puzzles similar to those at the top of this page.

Adverbs

Fill in the circle by the adverb that tells when or where.

1. Maya and I built our invention yesterday.
   - ○ Maya
   - ○ built
   - ⊗ yesterday

2. We made it upstairs in my room.
   - ○ We
   - ⊗ upstairs
   - ○ my

3. We had to start over often.
   - ○ had
   - ○ start
   - ⊗ often

4. Soon, we figured it out.
   - ⊗ Soon
   - ○ figured
   - ○ out

5. Next, we showed our parents.
   - ⊗ Next
   - ○ we
   - ○ parents

Home Activity Your child prepared for taking tests on adverbs that tell when and where. Read aloud a favorite story to your child. Have your child listen for adverbs that tell when and where.

Name _____

Add re- or **un-** to the word in ( ).
Write the new word on the line.

re- + do = <u>re</u>do
un- + clear = <u>un</u>clear

(build)

1. Mr. Ford will __**rebuild**__ the car.

(happy)

2. He is **unhappy** with the color.

(paint)

3. He will __**repaint**__ it.

(fills)

4. He __**refills**__ the car with gas.

(lock)

5. Don't forget to __**unlock**__ the door!

School + Home **Home Activity** Your child added the prefixes *un-* and *re-* to words. Ask your child to think of other words to which *un-* and *re-* can be added. Have him or her list the words and use them in sentences.

Name _____

Pick a word from the box to finish each sentence.
Write it on the line.

| poor   answered |
| different   carry |

1. The soil was so **poor** that nothing grew.

2. I **answered** all the questions about my garden.

3. All of the flowers were **different** colors.

4. I have to **carry** the garden tools to the backyard.

Pick two words from the box.
Write your own sentence using each word.

5. Children's sentences will vary. Check that children used one high-frequency word in each sentence.

6. _____

© Pearson Education, Inc., 1

Home Activity Your child learned to read and identify the words *answered, carry, different*, and *poor*. Encourage your child to make up a story that uses these words and draw pictures to illustrate the story.

Name _____

Read the story. **Answer** the questions.

This story is a folktale. It was passed along by the native people in the Philippines.

The Stars and the Moon

Long ago, the sky was close to the ground. A woman wanted to pound rice with her hammer. Before she started, she took off her beads from her neck. She took off the comb in her hair. She hung them both on the sky. Each time she raised her hammer, it would hit the sky. One time her hammer struck the sky so hard that the sky began to rise. It went up so far she lost her beads and comb. They never came back. The comb became the moon. The beads became the stars.

I. What is the big idea of the story?

how the moon and stars came to be

2. How did the woman change the sky and the ground?

She made the space between them bigger.

3. How do you know this is a folktale?

Possible answers: This couldn't really happen this way. It took place "long ago."

Home Activity Your child has learned about themes in stories. As you read stories with your child, discuss the big ideas in the stories.

Name _____

 My Piggy Bank

"Milk's all gone,"

said my older brother Sean.

He threw the jug in the trash can,

but I took it out and ran

right to the sink to wash it clean.

Then I used a marker to paint it green.

Now the jug's my very own piggy bank.

For that I have my brother Sean to thank.

Key Features of a Poem

• Many poems are shorter than a story.

• The lines in a poem often end with rhyming words.

© Pearson Education, Inc., 1

Name _____

Circle the word for each picture.

 p**ost**   g**old**   r**ind**   w**ild**

1.

(fold) fell

2.

kite (kind)

3.

(child) chilled

4.

mast (most)

5.

(cold) call

6.

fin (find)

7.

(wind) went

8.

(old) all

Circle the word to finish each sentence.

9. I (told) tied my baby sister a story.

10. I can't fine /(find) my pencil.

School + Home   **Home Activity** Your child read words with the long *o* sound as in *post* and *gold* and the long *i* sound as in *rind* and *wild*. Use each word in a sentence with your child.

Name _____

Words with Prefixes *un-, re-*

Circle a word to finish the sentence. **Write** it.

1. Will you   **unkind**   (**untie**)   my ribbon?

2. She looks   (**unhappy**)   **repay**.

3. Please   **refill**   (**reopen**)   the book.

4. She will   (**repay**)   **unhappy**   you.

5. Please   (**retell**)   **undress**   that story.

6. I will   **retell**   (**undress**)   the doll.

7. Please   (**rewind**)   **undo**   the movie.

8. Can you   **repay**   (**undo**)   this knot?

9. He is   **rewind**   (**unkind**)   to the dog.

10. He will   **retell**   (**refill**)   the glasses.

untie

unhappy

reopen

repay

retell

undress

rewind

undo

unkind

refill

Home Activity Your child spelled words to complete sentences. Read a sentence on this page. Ask your child to identify the word with the prefix *re-* or *un-* and spell it.

Name _____

Prepositions and Prepositional Phrases

A **preposition** is the first word in a group of words called a prepositional phrase.

Preposition	Momoko sat <u>on</u> the steps.
Prepositional Phrase	Momoko sat <u>on the steps</u>.

Circle the preposition in each sentence.
Say a new sentence using each preposition.

1. Susie read a book (about) gardens.

2. Susie wanted a garden (in) her yard.

3. She started working (before) school.

4. She planted flowers (after) school.

Write the prepositional phrase in the sentence.
Say other prepositional phrases that could replace it.

5. I got a good idea in the morning.

in the morning.

Home Activity Your child learned about prepositions. Read an article to your child. Have him or her identify prepositional phrases from the article.

© Pearson Education, Inc., 1

Name _____

Sequence

First

Next

Last

Home Activity Your child has planned a poem. Play a word game by making up phrases that rhyme with household words, such as *bed* (sleepy head) or *book* (take a look).

Name _____

Copy the **sentences**. Leave the correct space between words.

1. Please unfold the paper.

Please unfold the paper.

2. He will unlock the safe.

He will unlock the safe.

3. The store will reopen.

The store will reopen.

4. Rewrite your name.

Rewrite your name.

5. Let's unload the box.

Let's unload the box.

Did you leave the correct space between your words?   Yes   No

Home Activity Your child practiced writing sentences using words that begin with *un-* and *re-*. Write the following words on a sheet of paper and have your child read and rewrite them as neatly as possible: *rejoin, remake, unseen, unkind.*

Name _____

Look at the picture.
Read the introduction.
Write what each character will say.
Present the play.

One day, a boy walked into town. He was hungry.
He had a pot and a stone. He decided to make stone soup.

Stone Soup: The Play   **Responses will vary. Possible responses:**

Boy: I am going to make stone soup, but I need vegetables.

Farmer: Here are some carrots.

Woman: Here are some onions.

Young Girl: Here are some tomatoes.

Young Boy: Here are some potatoes.

Mule: Here is some water.

Boy: The soup is ready. Please have some.

Everyone: By working together, everyone enjoyed the soup.

School + Home

Home Activity Your child learned how to write a script. Together with your child, think of a favorite folktale, fairy tale, or other story that you enjoy. Work together to write a script based on the characters of the story. If possible, cast the characters and present the play as a family.

Name _____

Quincy's Bad Day

Prefixes *un-* and *re-*	Long *o* and Long *i*	High-Frequency Words	
unhappy	told	wild	you	the
unlocked	sold	kind	I	to
unwise	old	find	said	your
replace	folded	hope	a	some
restart	most			

"You look most unhappy," Jess told Quincy.

"I AM unhappy," Quincy said.

"Why?" asked Jess with a kind smile.

Jess folded her arms.

"It's unwise to stay sad," she said.

Let's restart your day and have some fun!"

4

Decodable Story *Quincy's Bad Day*
Target Skills Prefixes *un-* and *re-*; Long *o* and Long *i*

"First, Dad sold my old bike.
"I hope I can replace it."

"Then, the dog went wild.
He ran out the unlocked gate.
I didn't find him until just now."

Words with Prefixes *un-*, *re-*

Spelling Words					High-Frequency Words
unhappy	refill	untie	undo	repay	different
unkind	undress	retell	reopen	rewind	through

Write the prefix **un-** or **re-**. **Write** the list word.

1. Dad will __**re**__ tell the joke.   **retell**

2. I can __**un**__ tie my shoes.   **untie**

3. Let's __**un**__ do this puzzle.   **undo**

4. He was __**un**__ kind to Sam.   **unkind**

5. She is __**un**__ happy.   **unhappy**

6. You must __**re**__ pay the loan.   **repay**

7. The men will __**re**__ open the crate.   **reopen**

8. Can you __**re**__ wind the tape?   **rewind**

Write the word that rhymes.

9. parent __**different**__   10. blue __**through**__

Home Activity Your child wrote words with the prefixes *un-* and *re-*. Have your child name the base word in each list word and tell how adding the prefix changes the meaning.

© Pearson Education, Inc., 1

Prepositions and Prepositional Phrases

Imagine you are helping build a garden.

Write about what happens. **Use** prepositional phrases.

Possible response: My family has a garden on our roof. We grow vegetables in long boxes. I plant seeds in rows. Tomatoes climb up the posts.

Choose other prepositions. **Say** a sentence for each preposition.

Home Activity Your child learned how to use prepositions in writing. Take turns with your child writing sentences using prepositional phrases.

© Pearson Education, Inc., 1

Name _____

Words with Prefixes *un-*, *re-*

Spelling Words				
unhappy	refill	untie	undo	repay
unkind	undress	retell	reopen	rewind

Read the words in the box.
Add un- or **re-** to make a list word. **Write** it.

pay	tell
wind	fill

1. **repay**
2. **retell**
3. **rewind**
4. **refill**

Find a list word in each row of letters. **Circle** it. **Write** it.

5. r (u n t i e) s t   5. **untie**

6. t h (r e o p e n)   6. **reopen**

7. (u n k i n d) e s   7. **unkind**

8. x (u n d r e s s)   8. **undress**

9. w i (u n d o) t s   9. **undo**

10. s (u n h a p p y)   10. **unhappy**

© Pearson Education, Inc., 1

Home Activity Your child has been learning to spell words with the prefixes *un-* and *re-*. Help your child think of other words with these prefixes.

Name _____

Prepositions and Prepositional Phrases

Mark the word in each sentence that is a preposition.

1. The yard was bordered with homes like hers.
   - ○ The
   - ○ yard
   - ⊗ with

2. Except for old tires, the yard was cold and bare.
   - ⊗ Except
   - ○ tires
   - ○ the

3. The neighbors watched Momoko from their windows.
   - ○ neighbors
   - ⊗ from
   - ○ windows

4. Momoko planted the bulbs across the yard.
   - ○ Momoko
   - ○ bulbs
   - ⊗ across

5. People would sit and visit in the evenings.
   - ○ People
   - ○ sit
   - ⊗ in

Home Activity Your child prepared for taking tests on prepositions. Read aloud a favorite story to your child. Have your child say "Stop" each time he or she hears a prepositional phrase.

600 **Conventions** Prepositions and Prepositional Phrases

Writing Process Lessons

Name _____

Story Chart

Fill out this story chart to help you organize your ideas. **Write** your ideas in sentences.

_____

Title _____

Beginning

Answers will vary.

Middle

Answers will vary.

End

Answers will vary.

Name _____

Use Words That Tell How You Feel

Write a word from the box to tell how the writer feels.

Use each word one time. The pictures will help you.

Word Bank
happy
sad
scared
mad

1. My brother took my book.

    I feel _____ **mad** _____.

2. I won a prize.

    I feel _____ **happy** _____.

3. My best friend moved away.

    I feel _____ **sad** _____.

4. A dog growled at me.

    I feel _____ **scared** _____.

© Pearson Education, Inc., 1

Name _____

Adding a Word, Phrase, or Sentence

Read each set of sentences. **Answer** the question.

I. What word did the writer add? Write the word.

I saw a fish.

I saw a huge fish.

huge

2. What phrase did the writer add? Write the phrase.

The fish swam.

The fish swam into me.

into me

3. What sentence did the writer add? Write the sentence.

Then the fish swam away.

Then the fish swam away. I laughed.

I laughed.

Self-Evaluation Guide

Check *Yes* or *No* about voice in your story.

	Yes	No
I. I used words that tell how I feel.		
2. I used one or more words that describe.		
3. I used one or more words that show action.		

Answer the questions.

4. What is the best part of your story?

Answers will vary.

5. What is one thing you would change about this story if you could write it again?

Answers will vary.

Name _____

Letter Chart

Fill out this letter chart to help you organize your ideas.
Write your ideas in sentences.

Whom is the letter for?
_____
- -
 <u>**Accept all reasonable responses.**</u>

What is the main idea of the letter?
_____
- -
_____

What details support the main idea?
_____
- -
_____
- -
_____
- -
_____

Whom is the letter from?
_____
- -
_____

© Pearson Education, Inc., 1

Use Correct Letter Form

Write the date, greeting, and closing from the box to complete the letter. **Put** commas in the correct places. **Write** your name at the end.

Yours truly
May 4 2011
Dear Ms. Allen

May 4, 2011

Dear Ms. Allen,

You are a good worker. You are always there.

You make sure kids get to school safely.

Thank you.

Yours truly,

Child's name

© Pearson Education, Inc., 1

Name _____

Deleting a Word, Phrase, or Sentence

Read the sentences. **Follow** the directions.

I. The fire alarm was so so loud!

Delete, or take out, the word that is not needed. Write the sentence.

The fire alarm was so loud!

2. Juan was scared and afraid.

Delete the phrase that is not needed. Write the sentence.

Juan was scared.

3. Juan found out there was no fire. The firefighter said there was no fire.

Delete one sentence that is not needed. Write the other sentence.

The firefighter said there was no fire.

Name _____

Editing 1

Edit these sentences. **Look** for errors in grammar, punctuation, capitalization, and spelling. **Use** proofreading marks to show the corrections.

Proofreading Marks	
Delete (Take out)	ᔤ
Add	^
Spelling	⬭
Uppercase letter	≡
Lowercase letter	/

cross
1. The girls (cros) the street.

2. They need help ^(.)

3. Mr. james helps them.
    ≡

are
4. The girls is happy.
    ^

have
5. We (hav) many helpers.

Now you'll edit the draft of your letter. Then you'll use your draft to make a final copy of your letter. Finally, you'll publish your writing and share it with others.

Name _____

Main Idea and Details Chart

Fill in the chart with the main idea and details for your expository article. Write your ideas in sentences.

Main Idea

Detail

Detail

Detail

© Pearson Education, Inc., 1

Name _____

Strong Verbs

Add a strong verb from the box to each sentence.

> buzzes   gleams
> bends   paddles   splashes

1. The lake **gleams** in the sun.

2. A duck **paddles** to shore.

3. Water **splashes** on the rocks.

4. The grass **bends** in the wind.

5. A bee **buzzes** by my ear.

© Pearson Education, Inc., 1

Name _____

Adding or Deleting a Phrase or Sentence

Read the sentence. **Follow** the directions.

1. The birds fly.

   Add a phrase to the sentence. Tell where the birds fly. Write the new sentence.

   The birds fly in the sky.

2. The birds eat grass.

   Add a sentence. Tell why the birds eat grass. Write the new sentence.

   They are hungry.

3. The autumn leaves are red in the fall.

   Delete the phrase that is not needed. Write the new sentence.

   The autumn leaves are red.

4. There are a lot of trees in the woods. The forest has many trees. Some are tall, and some are short.

   Delete a sentence that is not needed. Write the other sentences.

   The forest has many trees.

   Some are tall, and some are short.

Editing 2

Edit these sentences. **Look** for errors in grammar, punctuation, capitalization, and spelling. **Use** proofreading marks to show the corrections.

Proofreading Marks	
Delete (Take out)	ꝛ
Add	^
Spelling	⬭
Uppercase letter	≡
Lowercase letter	/

waves
1. The beach has big ⟨wavs⟩.

2. It is named for a man, will rogers.
   ≡   ≡

Are
3. ~~Is~~ there shells in the sand?
      ^

4. The water feels very cold ⊙
                          ^

smells
5. The air ⟨smels⟩ like salt.

Now you'll edit the draft of your expository article. Then you'll use your draft to make a final copy of your article. Finally, you'll publish your writing and share it with others.

Name _____

Story Chart

Fill in this story chart to help you organize your ideas.
Write your ideas in sentences.

_____
- -
Title _____

┌─────────────────────────────────────┐
│ **Beginning**   │
│   │
│   │
│   │
│   │
└─────────────────────────────────────┘
                    ↓
┌─────────────────────────────────────┐
│ **Middle**   │
│   │
│   │
│   │
│   │
└─────────────────────────────────────┘
                    ↓
┌─────────────────────────────────────┐
│ **End**   │
│   │
│   │
│   │
│   │
└─────────────────────────────────────┘

Name _____

Good Adjectives

Add an adjective from the box to each sentence.

> loud   five
> tall   sunny   wild

1. It was a _____ **sunny** _____ spring day.

2. Maria heard _____ **loud** _____ quacks.

3. The _____ **wild** _____ ducks had a nest.

4. It was in the _____ **tall** _____ grass.

5. Maria saw _____ **five** _____ baby ducks.

Name _____

Adding or Deleting a Word or Phrase

Read the sentence. **Follow** the directions.

1. Tim walked.

   Add a phrase to the sentence. Tell where Tim walked. Write the new sentence.

   Tim walked to the store.

2. Tim got a game.

   Add a word to the sentence. Tell more about the game. Write the new sentence.

   Tim got a silly game.

3. Tim and Juan had fun with the ~~fun~~ game.

   Delete a word that is not needed. Draw a line through the word.

4. Tom left his game ~~and forgot it~~ at Juan's house.

   Delete a phrase that is not needed. Draw a line through the phrase.

Name _____

Editing 3

Proofreading Marks	
Delete (Take out)	�
Add	^
Spelling	⬭
Uppercase letter	≡
Lowercase letter	/

This is part of a realistic story. **Edit** this paragraph. **Look** for errors in grammar, punctuation, capitalization, and spelling. **Use** proofreading marks to show the corrections.

to
Lee loved ~~too~~ read. Her favorite book was about a girl and her

read
dog. Lee ~~readed~~ it every night. One day the book was lost. Lee

looked all over that night she was sad. She could not read her

sleep   **looked**
favorite book. She could not slep. Her pillow felt hard. She ~~look~~

glad
under it. There was her book! Lee was so gladd

Now you'll edit the draft of your realistic story. Next you'll use your draft to make a final copy of your story. Finally, you'll publish your writing and share it with others.

Name _____

K-W-L Chart

Fill out this K-W-L chart to help you organize your ideas. **Write** your ideas in sentences.

What We Know	What We Want to Know	What We Learned
Answers will vary.		

Name _____

Writing Trait: Sentences

• Use all kinds of sentences: statements, questions, commands, and exclamations.

• Use different beginnings. Don't start too many sentences with **the, he,** or **she.**

Write the letter of each sentence next to the word that identifies what kind of sentence it is.

(A) Who is Alexander Graham Bell? (B) He invented the telephone. (C) That's a wonderful invention! (D) Don't forget about his work with deaf people.

1. Statement: **B** 3. Command: **D**

2. Question: **A** 4. Exclamation: **C**

Rearrange the words in each sentence so it begins with the underlined word. **Write** the paragraph.

Example: She invented a new game last week.

Answer: Last week she invented a new game.

She played the game today. She changed it later. She likes it better now!

Today she played the game. Later she changed

it. Now she likes it better!

Name _____

Adding or Deleting a Word or Sentence

Read the sentence. **Follow** the directions.

1. Kate invented a toy.

   Add a word to describe the toy. Write the new sentence.

   ## Kate invented a funny toy.

2. The toy can sing.

   Add a sentence. Tell what else the toy can do. Write both sentences.

   ## The toy can sing.

   ## It can dance.

3. The first kite was a huge ~~giant~~ leaf.

   Delete a word that is not needed. Draw a line through the word.

4. The first Ferris wheel was 250 feet tall. ~~How tall is the Statue of Liberty?~~ Many people could ride on the Ferris wheel.

   Delete the sentence that does not belong. Draw a line through the sentence.

Name _____

Self-Evaluation Guide

Check **Yes** or **No** about sentences in your report.

	Yes	No
1. I used facts in my research report.		
2. I used different kinds of sentences.		
3. I used different beginnings for my sentences.		

Answer the questions.

4. What is the best part of your report?

Answers will vary.

5. What is one thing you would change about this report if you could write it again?

Answers will vary.